'Jill Humphries
Dept. of Philosophy

Physical Reality

The CONTEMPORARY ESSAYS Series

GENERAL EDITOR: LEONARD W. LEVY

Physical Reality

Philosophical Essays on Twentieth-Century Physics

Edited by
STEPHEN TOULMIN

HARPER TORCHBOOKS
Harper & Row, Publishers
New York, Evanston, and London

FOR
TREVOR AND LESLIE HANSON

PHYSICAL REALITY

First HARPER TORCHBOOK edition published 1970

LIBRARY OF CONGRESS CATALOG CARD NUMBER: 78–121086

Contents

v

Prefatory Note

THIS ANTHOLOGY is in some measure a tribute to the memory of the late Professor Norwood Russell Hanson, whose striking essay on the Copenhagen interpretation of quantum theory is included here. Proceeds from the volume will go for the benefit of his children, and I am happy to express my own personal gratitude to those of the contributors and publishers concerned who waived their copyright or accepted reduced reprint fees on this account.

In preparing the anthology I have also received valuable help and advice from many colleagues: there is room to mention here only Paul Feyerabend, who encouraged me to have the entire Planck-Mach exchange translated for this volume, and Ernest Nagel, who drew my attention to the Henriette Hertz Lecture by T. Percy Nunn, which I did not previously know.

STEPHEN TOULMIN

Lincoln, Mass.
December, 1968

Introduction

I

PHYSICS AND philosophy have had a continuous relationship, but a fluctuating one. Like some long-married couple, they have co-existed at times peacefully, at times acrimoniously. In certain periods, physical scientists have been content to acknowledge their partnership with philosophers, and even to see their own fundamental theories and methods as resting on "metaphysical foundations." During others, physics has given opponents of philosophy the weapons with which they have attempted to demolish and discredit the "iridescent fancies" of metaphysics. And in the course of the twentieth century, as we shall see in this anthology, physics has gone through periods of both kinds.

The greatest physicist of them all, Isaac Newton himself, derived warm satisfaction from the manner in which (as he saw it) science and theology dovetailed with one another and gave each other added strength; and he expressed the hope that a proper understanding of his dynamical and gravitational ideas "might work with considering Men, for the Belief of a Deity." In Newton's time, the customary association between physics and metaphysics—or, as our ancestors would have put it, between "natural philosophy" and "metaphysical philosophy"—was no accident, for the initial questions of the two subjects had been closely related; and for centuries the same men had worked in both fields without any sense of ambiguity. (The separate English word, "scientist," was in fact coined only in A.D. 1840: before that time, physicists were commonly referred to as "natural philosophers" or, more simply, as "philosophers.") In this dual role, physicist-philosophers like Plato, Descartes and Kant had been concerned both to arrive at a "fundamental explanation" of the character of the physical world and also to give an explicit account and rational justification of the standards which any such "fundamental explanation" must meet.

In this respect—as Max Planck recalls, in the first of the essays reprinted here—these men were playing their parts in a debate that had begun with Thales in the sixth century before Christ. Thus, when Lavoisier and Dalton built their "new system of chemical philosophy" on foundations taken from Newton's physical atomism, they were applying a formula first stated in classical times by Anaxagoras:

> Common usage misleads us in speaking of things as "coming-into-existence" and "going-out-of-existence." Properly speaking, nothing can come into or go out of existence: there is only a mixing-together and separating-out of things that exist permanently. So it would be more correct to refer to "coming-into-existence" as *mixture* and to "going-out-of-existence" as *separation*.

Plato, likewise, was deeply concerned with questions in planetary kinetics and matter theory; Descartes and Leibniz, along with Newton, were the joint founders of modern dynamics and the "physical world-picture" built upon it; while Kant made half a dozen distinguished contributions to astronomy and physical cosmology, before he even turned his hand to the three *Critiques*.

   Yet there have been those other times as well, when empirical science—interpreted positivistically—has been presented as the only assured system of human knowledge, in comparison with which all the products of metaphysics and theology were no better than speculation and wish fulfillment. "Why," men have asked in these phases, "should anyone waste his time and energy speculating about ultimate reality in general, or in the abstract, when we can build up a well-authenticated picture of the world in specific, concrete terms, on foundations taken from our actual experience?" Seen from this point of view, the one necessary task philosophers face is to demonstrate how the fundamental concepts of physics derive from, and can be led back logically to, the prior experiential basis that provides their final warranty. Once that has been done, it should be possible to strip away the superstructure of speculative concepts that served as a temporary intellectual scaffolding while physicists were building a science capable of standing without external support on its own self-validating foundation. A science for which this has been done would be a "metaphysics-free" system, and nothing less than this can satisfy fully the positivists' ideal for science.

Unfortunately, this "one necessary task" has, hitherto, proved easier to state than to carry through. Although the concepts of theoretical physics derive a justification *ex post facto* from their power to make retrospective sense of our experience, no philosopher has yet succeeded in giving a satisfactory "logical reduction" of theoretical concepts to "hard experiential data" alone. On the contrary, there is increasingly strong reason to think that this cannot be done. Our theoretical concepts always turn out in practice to have been framed *in advance of* the experiences that justify them: indeed, it has been indispensable that they should be framed in advance, if we are to pose any theoretically relevant questions about those experiences. And even when a given theory (e.g., Newtonian mechanics) has been firmly established and given a definitive logico-mathematical formulation, this has never exhausted the resources of physics. For other aspects of experience that call for the development of further theoretical systems (say, electromagnetism, or quantum mechanics) based on quite different fundamental principles have then forced themselves on our attention. So, after a while, the passion with which scientists have thrown themselves into anti-metaphysical campaigns has always worked itself out, and the pendulum has swung back toward a greater tolerance for philosophy.

II

The development of twentieth-century physics, up to the present time, illustrates very well this movement of "withdrawal and return." By the end of the nineteenth century, the joint successes of Newtonian physics and Daltonian chemistry—which we learned at school, as late as the 1930's, to refer to as "classical" physics and chemistry—had given most physical scientists a robust, though not unquestioning, confidence in the objectivity and finality of the Newtonian world-picture, metaphysical presuppositions and all. But, from 1900 on, a series of intellectual earthquake shocks shook this confidence, and physicists were provoked to reappraise the philosophical foundations of their theories. First came Einstein's special relativity, and Thomson and Lorenz's theory of electrons; this was followed by Rutherford and Bohr's picture of sub-atomic structure; and, finally, the transformation of physics culminated in Schrödinger and Heisenberg's new systems of wave mechanics and quantum mechanics. The critique that ensued was as much epistemological as scientific in character. Few nineteenth-century physicists had questioned the power of science to make discoveries about an order of "physical reality" independent of human tastes and skills, and as old as the universe itself. This sudden crumbling of the foundations induced a fresh intellectual modesty. It now seemed more prudent to moderate one's claims for science: to look for confidence and certainty only in the directly experienced "observables" from which theoretical ideas apparently derived their empirical confirmation, and to interpret theoretical concepts as "intellectual constructs," or even as "fictions," which were to be entertained on an "as-if" basis and used as instruments for organizing our experience with the greatest intellectual economy.

This new fit of modesty encouraged the revival of an older alliance, that between mathematical physics and philosophical positivism. Auguste Comte, the earlier prophet of a *philosophie positive*, had begun by teaching mathematics at the École Polytechnique, and had been markedly influenced by the work of the mathematical physicist, Fourier. In the present case, the scientific partners to the alliance were chiefly concerned with relativity theory, quantum mechanics and the probability calculus, while the philosophers in question were the "logical positivists" or "logical empiricists" associated with the Vienna Circle. Once again, there was a good deal of overlapping: Ernst Mach, John von Neumann and Hans Reichenbach worked both as scientists, or mathematicians, and as philosophers, and Mach himself was the prime influence on both parties. Having been trained as a physicist, and having done distinguished work on the propagation of supersonic shock waves, he devoted himself more and more to philosophy and history of science and became highly influential in his position as Professor of the Philosophy of Science at the University of Vienna. Many of the positivists philosophers of the 1920's and 1930's were, in fact, his pupils or immediate successors.

Unquestionably, this alliance greatly helped to hasten the acceptance of quantum mechanics, with its observation-oriented methodology that would have been so uncongenial to the realistically minded physicists of the late nineteenth century. By the late 1930's, indeed, John von Neumann had convinced many theoretical physicists that some extreme claims could be made on behalf of the new physics. Not only did it at last provide that "metaphysics-free" science for which so many of them had been seeking, since it professed only to establish and systematize mathematical correlations between empirical observables, but furthermore (he claimed) it was and would remain the last, definitive word on the foundations of physical theory, since its fundamental axiom—Heisenberg's Uncertainty Relation—brought scientists up against the ultimate limits of observation. Einstein alone among the leading architects of the new quantum theory was openly skeptical about these more extreme claims; and his reward was to be ignored and dismissed by his juniors as an old fogey who had been blinded to the truth of the new doctrines by a nostalgia for the deterministic certainties of classical physics. By the outbreak of World War II in 1939, physical theory had reached a philosophical equilibrium, and the positivist majority, led by Niels Bohr—with John von Neumann as their chief ideologue—was encountering only pockets of resistance from such seeming reactionaries as Albert Einstein and Louis de Broglie.

As in other fields of art and science, the resulting orthodoxy went into the deep freeze for the duration of the war, to be thawed out six years later by scientists of a new and younger generation. Over the subsequent twenty years the whole tone of theoretical discussion in physics has changed. Scientists whose training *began* after 1927 could scarcely think of Einstein and Heisenberg as threatening long-cherished intellectual presuppositions: after all, the ideas of those men formed the heart of the physics in which the new generation had been trained. Since 1946, therefore, there has been much less direct epistemological questioning and uncertainty among theoretical physicists, and the profession has regained something of its earlier nineteenth-century confidence that physics is an effective instrument for discovering genuine "external" realities.

Even among those who are still preoccupied with the philosophical foundations of quantum mechanics, supporters of the prewar orthodoxy have been increasingly on the defensive. Away from its Vatican in Copenhagen, at Niels Bohr's Institute for Theoretical

Physics, the question What new system of physical theory will come after quantum mechanics? no longer appears as blasphemous as it once did. Indeed, the arguments of John von Neumann are now generally admitted to have proved much less than was originally thought: certainly, they failed to demonstrate that the principles of quantum mechanics were the last, definitive word about our possible knowledge of the physical world. Since 1950, accordingly, the positivist interpretation of quantum theory has been under challenge, both from philosophers and from physicists. The current situation in physics—notably, the unexplained proliferation of so-called fundamental particles—calls for new and different styles of theory and explanation, and these will be arrived at (it now seems) only by a new and more profound analysis of the methodological program of theoretical physics itself. At the present time, that analysis is part of the unfinished business of theoretical physics and is a central concern of such men as Geoffrey Chew in the United States, David Bohm in England and J. P. Vigier in France. What its eventual outcome will be remains far from certain; but, at any rate, the range of options being considered goes far beyond the limits set by the positivist methodology dominant in theoretical physics during the interwar years.

III

The essays in this book cover all three phases in the philosophical development of twentieth-century physics. We begin with a remarkable exchange that took place, in the years 1910 and 1911, between Max Planck and Ernst Mach. In this exchange, one can see very clearly the lines along which opinion was hardening, following the shocks which the classical system of physics had received in the early years of the twentieth century.

Both Planck and Mach had been strongly influenced by the philosophical ideas of Immanuel Kant as developed by the great physicist and physiologist Helmholtz; but they went on from Kant's position in very different ways. Philosophically, Planck appears, on the face of it, far the more conservative of the two physicists: this fact is somewhat ironical, since his own direct contributions to theoretical physics—notably, his idea of the "quantum" of energy—

were eventually to prove so radical a break with the ideas of the older, classical system. Neither Planck or Mach, at any rate, was in any mood to claim that the science of physics can arrive directly at any real knowledge of "external reality" or "things-in-themselves": this much caution Kant had taught them both. The question that divided them was, just *how much less* the physical sciences should settle for. Planck argues that physics must always remain outward-looking. Even though there is no question of arriving directly at a well-founded knowledge of external realities, physicists should nevertheless aim to build up for themselves, progressively, an intellectual world-picture which can—in course of time—become a more and more reliable guide to the character of those inevitably hidden realities. Indeed (Planck argues), beyond a certain point there is no longer any sense in attempting to draw a distinction between "the real world," or objective "Nature," and "the ultimate world-picture of the eventual future." As a result, "Nature" becomes for Planck a kind of "limiting conception," toward which the theories of physics approach asymptotically, as toward an ideal limit.

For Ernst Mach, by contrast, the lessons of the new physics were more drastic. They served only to reinforce, in his mind, conclusions he had already arrived at earlier as a result of his own reflections on the psychology and physiology of sense perception. The proper course for physics was not to continue groping vainly after a meaningless and/or inaccessible population of "things-in-themselves." The methodology of physics (in Mach's view) would remain incomplete so long as physicists insisted on looking only outward: rather they should turn their attention back upon themselves and consider more candidly the relationship of their theoretical concepts to their own "sense impressions" or "sense observations." The time had therefore come to adopt a more critical attitude toward the interrelationships between the *observing scientist* and his *objects of observation;* and at first sight Einstein's new emphasis on the role of the "observer" and the "frame of reference" in shaping the structure of physical theory appeared a striking corroboration of Mach's ideas. For all Max Planck's originality as a physicist, accordingly, progressive-minded young physicists were soon tempted to class him with Albert Einstein as a philosophical reactionary.

The next four essays in the present collection are taken from the years between the two world wars. In them, one sees the philosophical positivism of Mach gradually working its way into the fabric of theoretical physics and shaping the methodological orthodoxy of quantum mechanics, as expressed most strikingly in the writings of Niels Bohr. The first two essays are written from a philosophical rather than a scientific standpoint. The Henriette Hertz Lecture by T. P. Nunn, on "Anthropomorphism and Physics," gives an excellent epitome of the current situation in the philosophy of physics immediately before the scientific triumph of Heisenberg's quantum mechanics. Though Nunn pays flattering attention to the views of Max Planck, and even writes in terms suggesting that he is simply bringing Planck's argument up to date, the influence of Mach's sensationalist epistemology (as transmitted by Russell and the English "sense-datum" philosophers) shines through his argument. Intellectually speaking, the result is a somewhat eclectic compromise; but the essay is nonetheless valuable as an historical record, showing how far Mach's inward-looking approach to the experiential basis of physical theory had established itself in the philosophy of physics even before the explicit formulation of Heisenberg's ideas.

The essay by Moritz Schlick is one of the earliest, and in many ways still one of the best, analyses of the implications for philosophy of Heisenberg's new physical theories. Schlick had succeeded Mach both officially, in his professorship at Vienna, and unofficially, as the leader of the positivist school. As patron of the Vienna Circle, he preserved in his teachings all the spirit, and much of the content, of Mach's philosophy. For understandable reasons, Schlick chooses to concentrate his analysis in this essay on the question of "causality": the famous Uncertainty Relation, or Principle of Indeterminacy, was the element in Heisenberg's theory that appeared to break most completely with the presuppositions of the nineteenth-century classical system. But the essay touches, by implication, on most of the philosophical issues which were in dispute as a result of the development of relativity theory and quantum mechanics. The other two essays in this set (dating from 1935) represent an intellectual flurry between Albert Einstein and Niels Bohr over the intellectual adequacy and finality of quantum-mechanical explanations. At the time, Einstein's attack was regarded by theoretical physicists of the orthodox party as the last, dying twitch of nineteenth-century conservatism: in consequence, Bohr replied to Einstein in the spirit of a patient schoolmaster confronted by a basically intelligent but slightly wrong-headed pupil, and was led to spell out the philosophical assumptions of his position explicitly, and with great lucidity.

From the standpoint of the late 1960's, however, this skirmish between Einstein and Bohr appears more of a holding action, pending the moment for a counterattack. And the final set of three essays shows the pendulum beginning to swing back from the interwar positivism toward a more "realistic" position. Out of a substantial recent literature, I have chosen to include here three pieces notable for the quality of their arguments and for their readability. True to Hegel's saying that "The Owl of Minerva flies only at the dusk," we find Norwood Russell Hanson setting out the fullest and most balanced defense of the orthodox, Copenhagen interpretation of quantum mechanics in the late 1950's, just at the moment when its earlier dogmatic and exclusive claims had become manifestly indefensible. Hanson himself was primarily a philosopher, and his own argument is a temperate one. Unlike some of Bohr's closest pupils, he makes no attempt to revive John von Neumann's more extreme claims, but is content to spell out the full difficulties to be overcome by anyone who claims to supersede Heisenberg's system.

Scientifically speaking, Hanson is still defending the same quantum mechanics that Heisenberg had formulated thirty years earlier; but the philosophical standpoint from which he does so is very different. The earlier positivist stance is now abandoned, and the philosophical spirit in which Hanson argues would perhaps have been more congenial to Max Planck than to Ernst Mach. For he presents quantum mechanics as one more step in the continuing sequence of "world-pictures," by which physics progressively leads us toward Planck's intellectual ideal of a "Nature" conceived in terms wholly independent of human sense perception and the intellectual idiosyncrasies of particular men and cultures. Without abandoning the scientific fruits of Heisenberg's work, Hanson reinterprets its philosophy and methodology in a more "realistic" spirit.

On this new basis we may be obliged to acknowledge that Heisenberg's theories *could in principle* be superseded, but we shall be entitled to claim all the more strongly that they *will in fact* be very hard to displace.

All the same, as the intellectual difficulties facing physics have accumulated, the pressure on theoretical physicists to consider alternatives to Heisenberg's system more seriously has begun to build up. The two final essays included here discuss just one of the lines of thought which are currently being explored in this direction—that proposed by David Bohm of London. We have no particular reason at present to conclude that Bohm's theoretical approach is going to succeed more completely, or more quickly, than its rivals: indeed, Bohm's ideas about a "sub-quantum" world might yet prove as abortive as (say) William Prout's speculations, back in 1815, about the possible substructure of chemical atoms. Nevertheless, this line of attack is particularly worth noticing here, for three reasons. In the first place, David Bohm is philosophically one of the most articulate and self-aware of contemporary theoretical physicists: his approach to the current difficulties in theoretical physics shows a profound and explicit understanding of the methodological issues involved. In the second place, Bohm's current work does not require us to re-start work on theoretical physics entirely from scratch: rather, his dissent from the Copenhagen orthodoxy links him directly back to the prewar conservatism of Einstein and de Broglie. Finally, Bohm is a man whose professional grasp of quantum theory proper cannot be faulted: before leading the opposition to the orthodox positivist interpretation, he had in fact written one of the outstanding textbooks on quantum mechanics. In any case, whatever the final verdict on his constructive ideas, David Bohm has earned a place in the history of physics for his critical achievements; for it was he who reanalyzed John von Neumann's arguments about the logical finality and completeness of the quantum-mechanical system and was the first to make clear just how much those arguments did—and did not—establish.

IV

During the first two-thirds of the twentieth century, economic and sociological forces have largely fragmented the academic profession, and, as a result, we take for granted today institutional and organizational divisions between "physics" and "philosophy," and between the subdivisions of each area, of a kind that would have been unintelligible to the men of earlier generations. So it can be refreshing to turn back to the writings of Planck and Mach and to read again the arguments of men for whom physics and philosophy were part of a single all-embracing intellectual quest. This helps us to remember that current academic divisions have grown up more as a matter of administrative convenience and "career structure" than as a reflection of insuperable intellectual distinctions between the subject matters and questions of different fields.

Physics and philosophy have, in fact, continued to interact and even to overlap. If we write the history of philosophy during the twentieth century, we cannot afford to overlook, for instance, the debt which Ludwig Wittgenstein owed to the writings of Heinrich Hertz and Ludwig Boltzmann, the men from whom he learned physics in his youth. For the philosophical ambitions that the young Wittgenstein formulated for analytical philosophy were an intellectual extrapolation of those which Hertz and Boltzmann—themselves greatly influenced by Kant—had earlier conceived for theoretical physics. Conversely, physical cosmologists who write about the size and age of the universe at the present time are, inevitably, as troubled as ever by the philosophical antinomies that arise at the moment we attempt to discuss "the beginning of Time" or "the entirety of Space"—antinomies to which Immanuel Kant, writing out of bitter firsthand experience, devoted considerable space in his *Critique of Pure Reason.* After all, the fundamental questions in "natural philosophy" remain in our own time what they have always been. As theoretical physicists, our goal is to arrive at as comprehensive and fundamental account as we can achieve of the constitution and workings of the natural world; as philosophers of physics, our task is to state as explicitly as we can the character which such a "comprehensive and fundamental" explanation should—and can—possess.

These tasks are complementary rather than conflicting. The recurrent positivist belief, that the aims and methods of physics and metaphysics are essentially opposed, is seen in retrospect to be a hangover from the days when scientific innovations had to establish

themselves in the face of violent criticism from the advocates of
natural theology. But that was a passing phase of intellectual history. In the twentieth century, the philosophy of physics has returned to its original, and more respectable, role: as a scrutiny of
the intellectual methods and goals implicit in the construction of a
"comprehensive and fundamental" system of physical explanation.
This was the point of union between physics and metaphysics for
Plato, Descartes and Kant; and it remains the point of union between the subjects for the authors whose essays are reprinted in this
collection.

Some people may question whether it is desirable any longer for
the twin roles of physicist and philosopher to be united in a single
man; and one may grant in reply that, in practice, a preoccupation
with methodological or "philosophical" questions can, in some
cases, hinder rather than help physicists in the solution of their
properly scientific problems. Yet such a preoccupation is not universally crippling. On the contrary, even today some of the most able
and profound theoretical physicists seem to be all the better for
combining the roles of epistemologist and mathematician, or those
of philosopher and experimenter. Certainly, if I may end on a
personal note, the task of editing this collection has convinced me of
one thing: that, as theoretical physics enters the final third of the
twentieth century, it remains as entitled as ever to its traditional
name of "natural philosophy." For my own part, I would guess that
physicists will find a way out of many of their current theoretical
impasses, as much through an epistemological reanalysis of their
methods and presuppositions as through the accumulation of new
experimental data or the invention of new mathematical techniques. At the very least, the present essays may have the value of
reminding those of us who have learned to think of, for example,
Planck, Einstein and Bohr only as mathematicians or experimenters
that, for these men themselves, much of the profoundest significance
of their work lay rather in its philosophical foundations and
implications.

1

The Unity of the
Physical World-Picture

by MAX PLANCK

EDITORIAL NOTE: *In his book,* The Aim and Structure of Physical Theory, *Pierre Duhem showed how, in nineteenth-century France, the dominance of Cartesian rationalism over French philosophy had its counterpart in the intellectual habits and tastes of theoretical physicists, while the empiricism and pragmatism of the British philosophical tradition was likewise dominant in the physics of contemporary Scotland and England. Thus, from Ampère on, French electrical theorists expounded their subject in a strict axiomatic form, modeled as rigorously on the geometry of Euclid as Descartes could have asked; while Faraday, Maxwell and their colleagues in nineteenth-century Britain were equally given to arguing in terms of mechanical models, and regarded such models as an indispensable element in any complete physical explanation. (William Thomson, Lord Kelvin, had gone so far as to stand Vico's dictum* certum quod factum *on its head, declaring that he could not accept any explanations of natural phenomena as intelligible unless he could use them as the basis for a mechanical replication of the phenomena in question—*certum quod facibile.)*

Max Planck's Leiden lecture, reprinted here, shows how far, in Germany also, contemporary theoretical physics was developing within the framework of a philosophical tradition. The problem of physical reality—stated by Planck, and pursued by Ernst Mach in the next essay—is clearly presented here as a problem in post-Kantian philosophy. The question for both men is this: "Granted

1

that we can have no direct knowledge of things-in-themselves in complete isolation from the work of the creative intellect, what kinds of knowledge and certainty can we then aim at in theoretical physics?" Planck's answer to that question is a twofold one. On the one hand, he declares that we should aim at a "world-picture" in which all the constituent elements are interconnected by necessary inferences (this is the force of his term "unity") and which "reflects actual natural processes" in a way quite independent of "arbitrary" and "anthropomorphous" features: in this respect he follows Kant, insisting that the goal of physical theory must be the same for all rational thinkers whatever—even for inhabitants of Mars! On the other hand, he deviates from Kant in acknowledging that men do not (and cannot be expected to) arrive at this ideal world-picture all at once: it is at best an ultimate goal toward which physicists are always working, but which they approach only bit by bit, progressively eliminating from the laws and concepts of physics all references to specifically human, terrestrial or otherwise arbitrary elements.

The central sections of the essay are a discussion of the two principles of thermodynamics as reinterpreted by Ludwig Boltzmann. These two principles were, in Planck's eyes, the finest fruit of nineteenth-century physical thought, since they were the first completely universal and general laws of nature, and he uses them as type examples to illustrate his account of the ultimate goal of theoretical physics. Both laws (he argues) were first suggested to men by considerations of practical experience, and even by actual sensations; yet the whole tendency of intellectual developments in thermodynamics has been to generalize the theory, eliminating from it all the original allusions to, for instance, what we human beings can or cannot do. As Boltzmann has left them, the laws of thermodynamics thus provide a universal description of the general patterns according to which reversible and irreversible processes respectively conform in nature, and as such they must form elements in the "physical world"—or, to say the same thing, in the "ultimate physical world-picture"—of any rational post-Kantian physicist.

In conclusion, Planck criticizes the ideas of Ernst Mach, which were finding a considerable following among scientists and philosophers around the turn of the century. As we shall see in the next essay, Mach was as insistent on maintaining the links between physical concepts and human sensations as Planck was on eliminating them; and the skeptical doubts which had prompted Mach to take this position had made him question, equally, the reality of atoms and the universal applicability of physical laws derived from human experience. Planck himself, however, was concerned, philosophically speaking, less with epistemological than with ontological or transcendental issues, and Mach's scruples struck him as excessive and potentially damaging. It was all very well to be cautious and critical in the claims made on behalf of any actual *theory; but, as an* ideal, *the record of history shows that the conception of a "unified physical world-picture," devoid of specifically man-centered features and so the same for any rational "physical thinker," had more than proved its worth.*

GENTLEMEN: WHEN I received your kind invitation to address you here on some aspects of my studies, my first thought was how diligently physics is studied here in Holland, what distinguished and world-famous names you have constantly before you as shining examples, and how little really new material a lecture on theoretical physics, here in Leiden of all places, can have to offer you. In attempting nevertheless to hold your attention for a while, I take courage from the reflection that our science, physics, approaches its goal not by a direct route but by many winding paths, and that in a physical research there is wide scope for individuality. One man works here, another there, one uses this method, another that, and the physical world-picture at which we are all working is depicted somewhat differently by each of us. So I hope to hold your interest if I now try to outline the main features of the physical world-picture as it has been shaped, and will presumably continue to be shaped, by the experiences and opinions at my disposal.

I

From time immemorial, as long as there has been any natural science, its ultimate supreme goal has been the combination of the motley diversity of physical phenomena into a unified system or even a single formula; and from time immemorial there have been two opposite methods of solving this problem. These have often been in conflict, but have more often corrected and cross-fertilized one another, particularly when united in a joint endeavor by a shared spirit of inquiry. One method is more youthful in character. It grasps boldly at the whole, speedily generalizing from individual experiences, and immediately concentrates on a single concept or proposition, within which it attempts with more or less success to confine the whole of nature and all its manifestations. Thus Thales of Miletos took "water," Wilhelm Ostwald "energy" and Heinrich Hertz the "principle of the straightest path" as focal points of their physical world-pictures, in which the connection and explanation of all physical events were to be found.

The other method is more cautious, modest and reliable, but it is less forceful than the first and took much longer to be accepted. To begin with, it does not aim at conclusive results; it adds to the picture only those individual features which appear to be completely guaranteed by direct experiences, leaving their further elaboration for later investigation. This method found its most significant expression in Gustav Kirchhoff's well-known definition of the task of mechanics as a "description" of the motions taking place in nature. These two methods complement one another, and physical research could not dispense with either of them.

But I do not wish to talk now about this dual methodology of our science, but rather to draw your attention to the more fundamental question to which this particular methodology has led us and will no doubt continue to lead us. No one can seriously deny that great progress has been made in the development of physics, or that we come to know more about nature every decade—this is proved by a single glance at the means, increasing in number and significance, by which man has learned to make nature serve his ends. But in what direction is this progress leading us? To what extent can one say that we are truly approaching our desired goal, a unified system? This question is bound to be of the greatest importance to any physicist who wishes to keep in touch with developments in his field. And, if we are able to obtain information on these questions, we shall also be in a position to consider the further question, nowadays a highly controversial one: What do we really mean when we speak of a physical world-picture? Is it merely a convenient but basically arbitrary intellectual concept, or should we take the opposite view, that it reflects actual natural processes quite independent of us?

There is only one way of discovering in which direction physical science is developing: by comparing its state today with that in an earlier epoch. If we go on to ask what external characteristic gives the best indication of the state of development of science, I can think of none more universal than the way in which it defines its basic concepts and separates its various branches. For, as is clear to all thoughtful people, the latest and most mature results of research are, often enough, already implied in definitions and in the mode of division of the subject matter.

Let us see what has happened in physics in this respect. First of all, we observe that all branches of scientific physical research are derived from purely practical needs or from particularly remarkable natural phenomena. The original subdivision of physics and the names of its separate branches result from these points of view. Thus geometry developed from land surveying, mechanics from engineering, acoustics, optics and heat theory from the corresponding sense perceptions, electrical theory from the curious behavior of rubbed amber, and magnetic theory from the remarkable properties of the iron ore found near the town of Magnesia. True to the law that all our experiences are derived from our sense perceptions, the physiological element is predominant in all physical definitions. To sum up: in its origins the whole of physics, its definitions as well as its entire structure, is in a sense anthropomorphous in character.

How different is the picture presented by the doctrines of modern theoretical physics! At first sight they appear much more unified. The number of separate branches of physics is much reduced, because related branches have been combined; thus, acoustics has been completely merged in mechanics, and magnetism and optics in electrodynamics. This simplification has been accompanied by a pronounced withdrawal of the human-historical element from all physical definitions. What physicist of today associates electricity with rubbed amber, or magnetism with the site in Asia Minor where the first natural magnets were found? Specific sense impressions have been completely eliminated from physical acoustics, optics and thermodynamics. Physical definitions of tone, color and temperature are no longer derived from the immediate impressions of the corresponding senses. Tone and color are defined in terms of frequencies or wavelengths. Temperature is defined, theoretically, in terms of temperature scale derived from the second law of thermodynamics; in the kinetic theory of gases by the kinetic energy of molecular movement; and for practical purposes by the change in volume of a thermometric substance or by the deflection of a bolometer or thermo element. In none of these cases is temperature nowadays associated with the sensation of heat.

The same thing has happened to the concept of force. The word "force" undoubtedly originally meant *human* force. This is because the first and earliest machines—the lever, the roller, the screw— were driven by men or animals, and it shows that the concept of force was originally derived from a sense of exertion or muscular strain—that is, from a specific sensation. But in the modern definition of "force" the specific sensation appears to have been eliminated, just as color sense has been eliminated from the definition of color.

Indeed, this suppression of the specific sensory element from the definitions of physical concepts has gone so far that areas of physics which formerly owed their unity to their association with particular sense impressions are now divided into a number of independent parts, against the general trend toward unification and fusion. Heat theory is the best example of this. Formerly, heat constituted a specific, well-defined, homogeneous branch of physics, characterized by the impressions of the thermal sense. Today, we find that in practically all textbooks a whole branch of thermophysics—radiant heat—is dealt with separately under the heading of optics. The thermal sense is no longer sufficiently important to hold the heterogeneous parts together; on the contrary, one part is attached to optics or electrodynamics and another to mechanics, in particular to the kinetic theory of matter.

Looking back, we can summarize all this by saying that the whole development of theoretical physics until now has been marked by a unification achieved by emancipating the system from its anthropomorphous elements, in particular from specific sense impressions. But if we reflect, on the other hand, that these impressions are the recognized starting point for all physical research, this conscious turning away from basic presuppositions must appear astonishing and even paradoxical. And yet there is hardly a fact in the history of physics as manifest as this one. Truly, what inestimable gains must have been required to justify such a fundamental self-renunciation!

Before we examine this important point more closely, let us turn from the past and present to the future. How will the system of physics be subdivided in coming centuries? At present, it still has two large independent branches: mechanics and electrodynamics, also known respectively as the physics of matter and the physics of ether. The former includes acoustics, bodily heat and chemical phenomena; the latter magnetism, optics and radiant heat. Will this division be final? I do not think so, since the boundaries of these two branches cannot be precisely defined. For example, are the processes of light emission part of mechanics or electrodynamics? And in which branch should we classify the laws governing the motion of electrons? At first sight we might say: electrodynamics since, in the case of electrons, ponderable matter plays no part. But suppose we look more closely at the movement of free electrons in metals. We find, for instance, in studying the experiments of H. A. Lorentz, that their laws fit much better into the kinetic theory of gases than into electrodynamics. Altogether the original distinction between ether and matter seems to me to be disappearing. Electrodynamics and mechanics are by no means so sharply divided as is widely assumed in some circles, where there is even talk of a conflict between the mechanical and electrodynamical points of view. In principle, mechanics really needs for its basis only the concepts of space, of time and of whatever moves, whether we describe it as a substance or a state. But electrodynamics cannot do without these same concepts either. An appropriately generalized conception of mechanics could therefore very well include electrodynamics. Indeed, there are many indications that these two areas, which already overlap, will end by being combined into a single subject—general dynamics.

Once the gap between ether and matter has been bridged, what viewpoint will then provide a definitive foundation for the subdivision of the system of physics? It follows from what we have just observed that this question will determine the whole character of the future development of our science. To study it more closely we must go rather more deeply into the nature of physical principles.

II

In order to do this, I must ask you first to accompany me to the point from which the first step was taken toward the true realization of a unified system of physics, which had formerly only been postulated by philosophers: to the *principle of the conservation of energy*. For the concept of energy, together with those of space and time, is the only one common to all branches of physics. After all that I have said, it will be clear—indeed, almost self-evident—that, in its origin, the energy principle was also anthropomorphous in character, even before its general formulation by Mayer, Joule and Helmholtz. It has its first roots in the recognition that there is no way of getting useful work from nothing. This recognition comes mainly from the experiences accumulated in the attempt to solve a technical problem: the invention of a *perpetuum mobile*. In this way the *perpetuum mobile* has had as wide an influence on physics as alchemy had on chemistry, although science has profited not from the positive, but from the negative results of these experiments. Nowadays, our expression of the energy principle makes no reference to human or technological aspects. We say that the total energy of a closed system of bodies is a magnitude which cannot be increased or diminished by any events taking place within the system. We no longer regard the accuracy of this statement as dependent on the precision of the methods now available to us for the experimental investigation of the problem of the *perpetuum mobile*. In this generalization—which strictly speaking is not probable, but which forcibly imposes its authority on us—lies the emancipation from anthropomorphous elements referred to earlier.

While the energy principle confronts us as something complete and independent, quite separate from, and independent of, the chances of its evolution, this is by no means equally true of the principle which R. Clausius introduced into physics under the name of the second law of thermodynamics. The very fact that this law is only just hatched makes it of particular interest to our present discussion. In fact, the second law of thermodynamics, at least as generally understood, is still decidedly anthropomorphous in character. For there are many eminent physicists who connect its validity with man's inability to penetrate the elementary constituents of the molecular world and to emulate Maxwell's demons, who were able to separate the faster molecules of a gas from the slower ones without the expenditure of any energy, simply by sliding a small bolt to and fro. But one need not be a prophet to predict with certainty that, as the second law has nothing essentially to do with human abilities, its definitive formulation will and must make no reference to the feasibility of any natural process of human skill. I hope that the following remarks may contribute something to this emancipation of the second law.

Let us look a little more closely at the content of the second law, and its relation to the energy principle. While the energy principle limits the course of natural processes by never permitting energy to be created or destroyed, but only transformed, the second law goes even further and does not permit all kinds of energy transformations, but only certain kinds in certain circumstances. Thus, it allows mechanical work to be completely and directly transformed into heat, for example, by friction, but it does not allow heat to be transformed directly into work. For if that were possible, one could use the heat of the earth's surface, which is available in unlimited quantities, to drive a motor, with the double advantage that this motor would serve as a refrigerator, since it would cool the earth's surface.

From the empirically established impossibility of such a motor (also known as a *perpetuum mobile* of the second kind), it necessarily follows that there are occurrences in nature which cannot in any way be put into reverse. If, for instance, a friction process, by which work is changed into heat, could be *completely* reversed with the help of any apparatus (however complex), this apparatus would in fact be the motor just described: a *perpetuum mobile* of the second kind. This follows, if we reflect, from what the apparatus would achieve: the transformation of heat into work without any other residual change.

If we call such an occurrence, which cannot in any way be reversed, an "irreversible process," and all other occurrences "reversible processes," we can express the essence of the second law of thermodynamics by saying that there are irreversible processes in nature. Thus, changes in nature are all one-way: with each and every irreversible process the world takes a step forward, whose traces can never be completely obliterated. Examples of irreversible processes, besides friction, are thermal conduction, diffusion, electrical conduction, the emission of light and heat radiation, the atomic decay of radioactive substances, etc. Examples of reversible processes are the movements of the planets, free fall in a vacuum, the undamped movements of a pendulum, the propagation of light and sound waves without absorption or deflection, undamped electrical oscillations, etc. All these processes are either periodic, or can by appropriate means be completely reversed, leaving no residual change—e.g., the free fall of a body can be reversed by using the speed attained to bring it back to its original level; a light or sound wave by suitable reflection from perfect mirrors.

What are the general properties and characteristics of irreversible processes and what is the general quantitative measure of irreversibility? This question has been examined and answered in a variety of ways, and the study of its development offers a particularly illuminating insight into the typical evolution of a general physical theory. Just as man originally discovered the energy principle by way of the technical problem of perpetual motion, another technical problem—that of the steam engine—led to the distinction between reversible and irreversible processes. Although Sadi Carnot had an incorrect idea of the nature of heat, he recognized that irreversible processes are less economical than reversible ones; that in an irreversible process, an opportunity of gaining mechanical work from heat is left unused. What could follow more obviously than the idea of defining the extent of the irreversibility of a process in terms of the amount of mechanical work lost in it? In reversible processes the amount of work lost would of course be nil. This interpretation has in fact proved useful in certain special cases, for example, in isothermic processes, and is therefore still quite well regarded today; but for general purposes it has proved unusable and even misleading. This is because the question How much work is lost in a given irreversible process? cannot be answered precisely unless it is clearly stated from what source of energy the work should have been gained.

An example will make this clear. Thermal production is an irreversible process, or, as Clausius puts it: Heat cannot pass from a cooler body to a warmer one without compensation. What work, then, is lost when a quantity of heat, Q, passes by direct conduction from a warmer body of temperature, T_1, to a cooler body of temperature, T_2? To answer this question, we use this heat transfer to perform a reversible Carnot-cycle process between the two bodies, which act as heat reservoirs. In this way a certain amount of work is gained, and it is precisely this work that we are looking for, since, in the direct transfer of heat by conduction, this work is lost. But this amount of work has no precise value until we know where the work should be coming from—from the warmer body, from the cooler body, or from somewhere else. We must remember that the heat given off by the warmer body in a reversible cycle is not equal to that taken up by the cooler one, because a certain amount of heat is transformed into work. One might identify the amount of heat, Q, transferred by direct conduction equally well, either as that given off by the warmer body or as that taken up by the cooler body. According to which one chooses, one defines the amount of work lost in the conduction process as:

$$Q \cdot \frac{T_1 - T_2}{T_1} \text{ or } Q \cdot \frac{T_1 - T_2}{T_2}$$

Clausius recognized this indeterminancy and so generalized the simple Carnot cycle, by assuming the existence of a third heat reservoir whose temperature was indeterminate and therefore provided an indeterminate amount of work.[1]

So we see that the route followed to define the irreversibility of a process mathematically does not lead to the goal; and we also see the real reason for this failure. The question is expressed in unduly anthropomorphous terms; it is too much tailored to the needs of mankind, whose first concern is to obtain useful work. If we want a precise answer from nature we must approach it from a more general, and less economic, standpoint. We will now try to do this.

Let us observe any process occurring in nature. It leads all bodies taking part in it from a given initial state, which I will call state A, to a given final state B. The process is either reversible or irreversible—there is no third possibility. But whether it is reversible or

---

[1] R. Clausius, *Die mechanische Wärmetheorie*, Vol. 1 (Leipzig: 2nd ed., 1876) , p. 96.

irreversible depends on the nature of the two states A and B, and not on the way in which the process takes place. It is simply a matter of answering the question whether or not, once state B is reached, a complete return to state A can be accomplished in any way. If a complete return from B to A is not possible, that is, if the process is irreversible, then state B is distinguished in nature from state A by a specific property. I expressed this once, some years ago, by saying that nature has a greater "preference" for state B than for state A. So expressed, those natural processes are impossible for whose final state nature would have less "preference" than she has for the initial state. Reversible processes are a borderline case; in them, nature has an equal "preference" for the initial and the final state, and the transition between the two can take place in either direction.

It is now a master of finding a physical magnitude whose amount will serve as a universal measure of nature's preference for a given state. It must be a magnitude which can be directly determined from the state of the system under observation, without knowing anything about its previous history, as is the case with energy, volume and other properties. This magnitude would increase during all irreversible processes, but would remain unchanged during all reversible ones. The amount of change during a process would provide a general measure of the irreversibility of the process.

R. Clausius actually discovered this magnitude, and named it "entropy." Any system of bodies in any state has a certain entropy, and this entropy expresses nature's preference for the given state; in all processes taking place within the system it can only increase, never decrease. If we observe a process in which the system is affected by outside influences, we must view the bodies from which these influences originate as part of the system; then the above law will still apply. The entropy of a system of bodies is equal to the sum of the entropies of its separate bodies, and the entropy of a single body is found by Clausius's method, using a particular reversible cycle. Conduction of heat to a body increases its entropy by the amount of the quotient: (quantity of heat conducted) divided by (temperature of the body). Simple compression, on the other hand, does not change the entropy.

Let us return to the example discussed above, of the heat, Q, conducted directly from a warmer body, with temperature T_1, to a cooler one, with temperature T_2. During this process, the entropy of the warmer body decreases and that of the cooler body increases, as stated above; and the sum of both changes, that is, the change in the total entropy of the two bodies, is:

$$- \frac{Q}{T_1} + \frac{Q}{T_2} > 0$$

This positive quantity gives a non-arbitrary measure of the irreversibility of the heat-conduction process. Innumerable examples could be cited of this kind: one is provided by every chemical process.

Thus, the second law of thermodynamics, with all its consequences, becomes the *principle of entropy increase.* In the light of the foregoing discussion, you will understand why I proceed to express the opinion that, in the theoretical physics of the future, the first and most important division of all physical processes will be into reversible and irreversible processes.

Indeed, all reversible processes, whether they take place in matter or in the ether or in both, show a much greater resemblance to one another than they do to any irreversible process. This is clear even from a formal consideration of the differential equations governing them. In the differential equations of reversible processes, the time differential always appears as a direct power, reflecting the fact that the sign of time can also be reversed. This is equally true of pendulum oscillations, electrical oscillations, acoustic and optical waves, and of movements of point masses or electrons, as long as all kinds of damping are excluded. It is also true of the infinitely slow processes considered in thermodynamics, which consist entirely of states of equilibrium in which time plays no part; in other words, in which the null power (which must be viewed as a direct power) occurs. As Helmholtz has shown, all these reversible processes also have the property in common that they are completely represented by the principle of least action, which gives an unambiguous answer to all questions about their measurable course: to this extent, we can describe the theory of reversible processes as a completely closed one. On the other hand, reversible processes have the drawback that they are, one and all, merely ideal; in reality, there is not a single natural reversible process, since every natural occurrence involves friction or thermal conduction to a greater or lesser extent. In the field of irreversible processes, however, the principle of least action is no longer sufficient; for the principle of entropy increase introduces into the physical world-picture a completely new element, alien to the action principle, which calls for special mathematical treatment. It accounts for the one-way course of events, and the attainment of a final fixed state.

I hope that the foregoing considerations will suffice to make it clear that the distinction between reversible and irreversible processes is a much more profound one than that between mechanical and electrical processes, and that this difference is therefore better entitled than any other to form the chief basis for the classification of all physical events, and should be allotted the principal role in the physical world-picture of the future.

And yet the proposed classification requires a further essential improvement. For it cannot be denied that the system of physics described is still adulterated with a strong dose of anthropomorphism. In the definitions of irreversibility and entropy reference is made to the feasibility of certain changes in nature, and this really means that the classification of physical events is made dependent on the extent of man's experimental skill, which does not remain constant but is continually being improved. If the distinction between reversible and irreversible processes is really to be of lasting significance for all time, it must be considerably deepened and freed from all reference to human abilities. I would now like to discuss how this can be done.

III

The original definition of irreversibility suffers, as we have seen, from the serious defect that it is based on the assumption of a definite limit to human ability, whereas no such limit can be demonstrated in reality. On the contrary, the human race is making every effort to extend the present limits of its capacity even further, and we hope that at some future time we shall be able to do many things which to many people today perhaps seem impossible. Might it not happen that a process viewed, until now, as irreversible might quite soon prove, as the result of a new discovery or invention, to be reversible? Then the whole edifice of the second law would inevitably collapse, for, as can easily be proved, the irreversibility of each single process is a condition for that of all others.

Let us take a concrete example. According to the latest investigations, the curious agitated movement, easily perceptible under a microscope, of small particles in suspension in a liquid, known as Brownian molecular movement, is a direct result of perpetual collisions between the molecules of the liquid and the particles. If, by directing and ordering them with the aid of some very fine device, but without perceptible expenditure of energy, we were able to influence the particles in such a way that the disorderly movement became an orderly one, we would without doubt have found a way to convert part of the heat of the liquid, without compensation, into grossly visible and therefore usable kinetic energy. Would this not be in contradiction to the second law of thermodynamics? If this question could be answered in the affirmative, the law could no longer claim the status of a principle, since its validity would be dependent on the progress of experimental technique. It is clear: the only way to ensure the validity of the second law as a principle is to render the concept of irreversibility independent of all human associations.

Now, the concept of irreversibility refers back to that of entropy; for a process is irreversible if it is associated with an increase in entropy. Thus, the problem necessitates an appropriate improvement in the definition of entropy. According to Clausius's original definition, entropy is measured by a particular reversible process, and the weakness of this definition results from the fact that many such reversible processes, in fact all of them, are in fact unrealizable. It can with some justification be answered that we are considering, not real processes and a real physicist, but ideal processes, so-called *Gedankenexperimente* [thought experiments], and an ideal physicist who applies all experimental methods with absolute precision. But this is precisely the difficulty. What is the scope of such ideal measurements by an ideal physicist? The possibility of compressing a gas, using a pressure equal to that of the gas, and warming it from a heat reservoir at the same temperature as the gas, is intelligible with the help of an appropriate boundary transition; but whether, for instance, saturated steam can be turned to liquid reversibly by isothermic compression, without any part of the steam condensing, must seem doubtful. And even more striking achievements are attributed to the theorist's thought experiments in physical chemistry! With his semi-permeable barriers, which in reality exist only in quite special circumstances and then only approximately, he separates reversibly not only every possible type of molecule, whether in a stable or a labile state, but also oppositely charged ions from one another and from undissociated molecules. He is impeded neither by the enormous electrostatic forces opposed to such a separation, nor by the fact that in reality the molecules become partly dissociated, and the ions partly reunited, at the very outset of this separation. Indeed, it is astonishing that all these daring trains of thought have survived the experimental testing of their results.

On the other hand, if we reflect that, in all these results, every reference to the feasibility of these ideal processes has disappeared—there are only connections between directly measurable magnitudes like temperature, quantity, or heat, concentration, etc.—then we cannot rule out the hypothesis that the whole transitory introduction of such ideal processes may in fact be a detour, and that the real content of the law of entropy increase, with all its consequences, can be separated from the original concept of irreversibility, or from the impossibility of a *perpetuum mobile* of the second kind, just as the principle of the conservation of energy has been separated from the law of the impossibility of a *perpetuum mobile* of the first kind.

The achievement of this step—the emancipation of the concept of entropy from man's experimental arts and the consequent elevation of the second law to a genuine principle—was the life work of Ludwig Boltzmann. Briefly, it consists in relating back the concept of entropy to the concept of probability. This also explains the significance of the term I used earlier—the "preference" of nature for a given state. For nature prefers more probable states to less probable ones, and performs transitions only in the direction of greater probability. Heat passes from a body with a higher temperature to one with a lower temperature, because the state of uniform temperature distribution is more probable than any state of non-uniform temperature distribution.

The calculation of the precise degree of probability for each condition of a system of bodies is made possible by the introduction of atomic theory and of the statistical approach. The known laws of general dynamics, mechanics and electrodynamics, taken together, can then be applied to the interactions of single atoms.

By this reinterpretation—at a single stroke—the second law of thermodynamics is removed from a position of isolation, the mysterious character of nature's preference disappears, and the entropy principle becomes linked as a well-established theorem of the probability calculus to the introduction of atoms into the physical world-picture.

It cannot be denied that this further step toward the unification of our world-picture is once again achieved at the price of many a sacrifice. The chief sacrifice consists in renouncing any really complete answer to all those questions about the details of a physical event implicit in the use of a purely statistical method. For, if we calculate only in terms of mean values, we learn nothing about the individual constituents of which they are composed.

A second serious disadvantage seems to lie in the introduction of two different types of causal connections between physical states: on the one hand absolutely necessary, on the other merely probable connections. If a heavy liquid at rest seeks a lower level, this (according to the law of the conservation of energy) is a necessary consequence of the fact that it can only begin to move—i.e., gain kinetic energy—if the potential energy is decreased and its center of gravity is thus lowered. But, if a warmer body transmits heat to a cooler body which is in contact with it, this is only enormously *probable,* but in no way absolutely necessary; for one can conceive quite special configurations and velocities of atoms which would lead to precisely the opposite result. Boltzmann inferred from this that such peculiar occurrences, which are contrary to the second law of thermodynamics, might possibly be met with in nature, so he left room for them in his physical world-picture. But this is a point over which, in my opinion, we need not follow his example. For a nature in which such things happened as the flowing back of heat into the warmer body, or the spontaneous unmixing of two diffused gases, would not be nature as we know it. As long as we are dealing only with the latter, we shall do better not to admit such singular occurrences as possible, but on the contrary to seek, and accept as realized in nature, that general condition which excludes phenomena running counter to all experience. Boltzmann himself formulated that condition for the theory of gases; it is, generally speaking, the "hypothesis of elementary disorder"—in short, the assumption that the individual elements with which the statistical method operates remain completely independent of one another. With the introduction of this condition, the necessity of all natural events is restored. Its fulfillment leads directly, by the laws of the probability calculus, to the increase of entropy: thus, we can express the essence of the second law of thermodynamics, simply, as the *principle of elementary disorder*. In this formulation, the principle of entropy can no more lead to contradictions than the probability calculus from which it is derived.

What then is the connection between the probability of a system and its entropy? This follows straightforwardly from the proposition that the probability of two independent systems is represented by the product of the individual probabilities $(W = W_1 \times W_2)$, and their entropy by the sum of the individual entropies $(S = S_1 + S_2)$. Thus, entropy is proportional to the logarithm of probability $(S = k \, log \, W)$. This law opens the way to a new method, going far beyond the resources of ordinary thermodynamics, for calculating the entropy of a system in a given state. It extends the definition of entropy to include not only states of equilibrium (as they are almost exclusively viewed in ordinary thermodynamics) but also all dynamic states whatever. To calculate entropy we no longer need, as Clausius did, to perform a reversible process whose realizability always appears more or less in doubt; we are independent of human technical skills. In short, the anthropomorphous element is completely eliminated from this definition, and in this way the second law, like the first, is given a firm basis in reality.

The fertility of the new definition of entropy is apparent not only in the kinetic theory of gases but also in the theory of radiant heat. It has led to the establishment of laws which are in perfect agreement with experience. The fact that radiant heat has an entropy follows from the fact that a body which emits heat radiation undergoes a loss of heat, and thus a decrease in entropy. As the total entropy of a system can only increase, part of the entropy of the whole system must be contained in the heat radiated. Thus, every monochromatic ray has a definite temperature depending only on its brightness; it is the temperature of a black body emitting rays of the same brightness. The main difference between the theory of radiation and the kinetic theory is that, in the case of radiant heat, the elements whose disorder is indicated by the entropy are no longer atoms, as with gases; rather, they are those extremely numerous, simple, sinusoidal component oscillations, which we may regard as making up every light or heat ray, however homogeneous.

It is particularly notable that the constants appearing in the laws of heat radiation in free ether, like the constants of gravity, have a universal character and involve no reference to any special substance or any special body. Thus, one can use them to establish units of length, time, volume and temperature, which must of necessity retain their meaning for all time and for all cultures, even extra-terrestrial and extra-human ones. This, as is well known, does not apply to the units of our normal measuring system. Although these latter are normally expressed in absolute units, they are thoroughly adapted to the special circumstances of our present terrestrial civilizations: the centimeter is based on the present circumference of our planet, the second on its period of rotation, the gram on water (the main component of the earth's surface), temperature on the fundamental points of water. But the former constants are of such a kind that even the inhabitants of Mars, and indeed all intelligences extant in nature as we know it, must at some time encounter them—if they have not already done so.

I would like to draw attention to a further remarkable clarification which the concept of entropy has undergone, as a result of being linked with probability. The proposition cited above, that the probability of two systems is the product of the probabilities of the separate systems, is known to apply only when the two systems are mutually independent, as regards probability calculations; otherwise, the probability is different. Thus, in certain cases, one might suppose the total entropy of two systems was different from the sum of their separate entropies. The proof that such cases really occur in nature was, in fact, recently provided by Max Laue. Two completely or partially "coherent" light rays (originating from the same light source) are, according to the probability calculus, not mutually independent, because the component oscillations of the one ray are related to those of the other. Now, one could in fact devise a simple optical apparatus by which two coherent rays of any temperature could be transformed into two others with a greater difference of temperature. Thus, Clausius's old principle, that heat cannot pass from a cooler to a warmer body without compensation, does not apply to coherent heat rays. But the principle of increased entropy still applies; only the total entropy of the original rays is not equal to the sum of their separate entropies, but smaller.[2]

The same holds for the question posed above, about the possible transformation of Brownian molecular movement into usable work. For, in any case, a device which would direct and order the individual moving particles (whether or not technically feasible) would, as soon as it began to function, be in some sense "coherent" with the movements of the particles. Thus, there would be no contradiction of the second law if it succeeded in producing usable kinetic energy. We must only bear in mind that, in this case, the entropy of molecular movement should not simply be added to the entropy of the apparatus.

Such considerations show how carefully we must proceed in calculating the entropy of a composite system from the entropies of the parts of the system. Strictly speaking, we must first ask about each part of the system whether perhaps, in another part of the total system, there is a coherent component system; otherwise, quite unexpected occurrences, apparently contradicting the entropy principle, might take place in case of interaction between the two component systems. But if the two component systems did not interact, the mistake involved in overlooking their coherence would pass unnoticed.

Are we not involuntarily reminded by these singular phenomena, which result from coherence, of those mysterious mutual relationships in our mental life which often remain quite hidden and can safely be ignored, but which given particular combinations of external circumstances can produce quite undreamed-of consequences?

Yes: if we once allow our imagination free rein, we cannot brush

---

[2] M. Laue, *Ann. d. Phys.*, 20 (1906), 365; 23 (1907), 1, 795; *Verh. d. Dtsch. Physik. Ges.*, 9 (1907), 606; this periodical [*Phys. Zeitschr*], 9 (1908), 778.

aside the possibility that perhaps—at distances from our immediate physical world whose extent cannot be comprehended by any of our methods of measurement—there exist certain coherent bodies which, so long as they remain separate from our own, behave as normally as ours, but which, if ever they began to interact with them, could evoke seeming (though perhaps only seeming) exceptions to the entropy principle. In this way, the threat of a universal heat death posed by the second law—which has made this law uncongenial to many physicists and philosophers—could be averted, without affecting its general validity in any way. But even without this artificial source of intelligence, this threat does not seem to me to call for any anxiety, because of the boundless unlimited extent of the world accessible to our observation: surely, many far more urgent questions now demand our attention.

IV

I have attempted to indicate briefly some of the principal features which the physical world-picture of the future will probably exhibit. If we now look back at the transformations which this world-picture has undergone in the course of the development of science, and if we contemplate once again the characteristic features of this development, then we must admit that the world-picture of the future (as compared with the brilliant pageant of the original world-picture, which grew from the manifold needs of human life, and to which all the specific sense impressions made their contribution) appears noticeably pale and prosaic, and lacking in direct evidence; and this last seriously detracts from its usefulness to an exact science. Add to this the aggravating circumstance that a complete elimination of sense impressions is quite impossible—since we cannot shut off the acknowledged source of all our experience—in other words, that direct knowledge of the Absolute is out of the question.

What, then, is the special impetus which, in spite of these manifest disadvantages, gives the future world-picture such decisive superiority that it supersedes all previous ones? It is simply its *unity:* unity of all individual features, unity of all places and times, unity of all researchers, all nations, all cultures.

For, if we look more closely, the old system of physics was not like a single picture, but more like a whole picture gallery; since every class of natural phenomena had its own picture. And these different pictures did not all hang together; one could take any one of them away, without affecting the others. In the future physical world-picture, this will not be possible. It will not be possible to omit a single feature as inessential. Each one is an indispensable component of the whole and, as such, has a specific meaning for observed nature; while, conversely, every observable physical phenomenon must find its precisely appropriate place in the picture. In this respect, it differs essentially from ordinary pictures, which certainly need to correspond to the original in some particulars, but not in all—a distinction to which, in my opinion, physicists have not hitherto paid enough attention. Even in the latest writings on the subject, one sometimes finds such remarks as this: that when applying electron theory or the kinetic theory of gases, one must confine oneself to the present, since the theory claims to give only an approximate picture of reality. If this remark were interpreted as meaning that one cannot expect all consequences of the kinetic theory of gases to conform to the facts of experiment, this interpretation would lead to serious misunderstandings.

When, in the middle of the last century, Rudolf Clausius deduced, from the basic hypotheses of the kinetic theory of gases, that the speeds of gas molecules at normal temperatures were measurable in hundreds of meters per second, it was objected that two gases are very slow to mix with one another, and that local temperature variations in gases are likewise very slow to equal out. Clausius did not then claim, in support of his hypothesis, that it was intended to represent only an approximate picture of reality, and that one must not expect too much of it; by calculating the mean free path, he showed that the picture he had outlined truly corresponded with reality, even in the two particulars mentioned. For he well knew that the discovery of a single definite contradiction would irrevocably cost the new theory of gases its place in the physical world-picture; and the same is still true today.

The possibility of making these great demands on the physical world-picture is the source of that compelling force by which this world-picture is at last commanding general recognition, independently of the goodwill of the individual researcher, independently of nationalities and of centuries—indeed, independently of the human race itself. This last assertion will at first appear very bold, if not absurd. And yet if we recall (for example) our earlier conclusions about the physics of Martians, we must at least admit that this generalization is of the same type as those employed daily in physics, whenever we go beyond directly observable facts and draw conclusions that can never be tested by human observations; and that, accordingly, anyone who denies its meaning and validity thereby cuts himself off from the physicist's mode of thinking.

Surely no physicist questions the admissibility of the statement that a creature endowed with physical intelligence, and possessing a special sense for ultra-violet rays, would recognize these rays as being of the same kind as visible rays, even though up to now nobody has ever seen either an ultra-violet ray, or such a creature; and no chemist hesitates to attribute to the sodium on the sun the same chemical properties as the sodium on earth, although he cannot hope ever to fill his test tube with a salt of solar sodium.

By these last arguments, we have already begun to answer the questions I asked at the end of my introduction: Is the physical world-picture only a more or less arbitrary creation of our intellect, or are we driven to the opposite interpretation, namely, that it reflects real natural events which are quite independent of us? Or, to put this more concretely: Can we reasonably assert that the principle of energy conservation was valid in nature, before any man was able to think about it, or that heavenly bodies will still move according to the laws of gravity when our earth, with all its inhabitants, has disintegrated?

When, in view of all that I have said, I answer "Yes" to this question, I am well aware that this answer goes against one movement in natural philosophy, led by Ernst Mach, which at present enjoys great popularity in scientific circles. According to this movement, there is no reality apart from our own impressions, and all natural science is in the last resort merely an economical adaptation of our thoughts to our impressions, to which we are driven by the struggle for existence. The dividing line between the physical and the psychical is a purely practical and conventional one; the only "real" elements in the world are the impressions.[3]

[3] Ernst Mach, *Beiträge zur Analyse der Empfindungen* (Jena, 1886) , pp. 23, 142.

If we put this last statement alongside what we have learned from our review of the actual development of physics, we are forced to the curious conclusion that the characteristic feature of this development expresses itself through a progressive elimination from the physical world-picture of the "real" elements of the world. Otherwise, every conscientious physicist would have to take constant pains to mark off his own world-picture as something conceptually unique and totally distinct from all others; and if ever two of his fellow physicists, after conducting the same experiment quite independently, claimed to have reached opposite conclusions—as does sometimes happen—then he would be committing an error of principle if he inferred that at least one of them must be mistaken. For the disagreement might, equally well, be caused by a difference between their respective world-pictures. I do not believe that a true physicist would ever embark on such a curious train of thought.

Meanwhile, I freely admit that an empirically vast improbability does not, in practice, differ from an impossibility of principle: I would like to emphasize this fact all the more positively, because the attacks made from that quarter [viz., Mach] against atomistic hypotheses, and against the theory of electrons, are unfounded and untenable. Indeed, I would like to oppose them by asserting—and I know that I am not alone in this—that atoms, little as we know of their detailed properties, are no more and no less real than the heavenly bodies, or the earthly objects which surround us. When I say: "A hydrogen atoms weighs $1.6 \times 10^{-24}g$," this statement expresses a kind of knowledge no less meaningful than the statement that the moon weighs $7 \times 10^{25}g$. Of course, I cannot place a hydrogen atom on the scales, nor can I even see it; but I cannot place the moon on the scales either, and, as regards seeing it, invisible heavenly bodies too are known to exist whose volume can be more or less precisely measured. Indeed, the volume of Neptune was measured before any astronomer had ever turned his telescope toward it. No system of physical measurement exists from which all knowledge based on induction is eliminated; this is true even of direct weighing. A single glance into a precision laboratory shows us how many experiences and abstractions are comprised in one such measurement, simple as it may appear.

It remains for us to ask why the Machian theory of knowledge has achieved such wide circulation among natural philosophers. If I am not mistaken, it represents at bottom a kind of reaction against the high hopes which a generation ago, after the discovery of the energy principle, were attached to the specifically mechanical view of nature—as recorded, for instance, in the writings of Émile du Bois-Raymond. I do not mean to deny that these hopes produced a number of outstanding achievements of permanent value—I need only mention the kinetic theory of gases—but, taken as a whole, they have proved exaggerated. Indeed, by introducing statistics into its considerations, physics has renounced the complete realization of the mechanics of atoms. Mach's positivism was a philosophical manifestation of unavoidable disenchantment. It deserves full credit for having rediscovered, in the face of a menacing skepticism, the one legitimate point of departure for all natural science in the sense impressions. But when it degrades the whole physical world-picture along with the mechanical one, it overshoots the target.

Although I am firmly convinced that Mach's system, if it is pursued with complete consistency, cannot be proved to contain any inner contradiction, it seems to me just as certain that its significance is, at bottom, only a formalistic one, which does not affect the essence of natural science. This is because the outstanding characteristic of all scientific research—the demand for a *constant* world-picture, independent of changing times and peoples—is alien to it. The Machian principle of continuity is no substitute for this; continuity is not constancy.

A constant, unified world-picture is, as I have tried to show, the fixed goal which true natural science, in all its forms, is perpetually approaching; and in physics we may justly claim that our present world-picture, although it shimmers with the most varied colors imparted by the individuality of the researcher, nevertheless contains certain features which can never be effaced by any revolution, either in nature or in the human mind. This constant element, independent of every human (and indeed of every intellectual) individuality, is what we call "the Real." Or is there today a single physicist worthy of serious consideration who doubts the reality of the energy principle? Rather, the recognition of this reality is nowadays a prerequisite for winning any scientific respect.

Certainly, one cannot establish general rules to indicate how far we may carry our confidence that we have determined the main features of the world-picture of the future. The greatest caution is called for here. However, these questions are only secondary ones. What really matters is that we recognize such a fixed goal, even if it can never be quite attained: this goal is not the complete adaptation of our ideas to our impressions, but *the complete liberation of the physical world-picture from the individuality of the creative mind.* This is a paraphrase, in rather more precise terms, of what I previously called the emancipation from anthropomorphous elements; we should not be misunderstood as implying that the world-picture ought to be completely detached from the creative intellect itself, which would be an absurd conclusion.

Finally, one more argument, which will perhaps make more impression on those who are still inclined to adopt the "human-economical" point of view as the really decisive one than all the foregoing objective considerations. When the great masters of the exact sciences introduced their ideas into science: when Nicolaus Copernicus removed the earth from the center of the universe, when Johannes Kepler formulated the laws which bear his name, when Isaac Newton discovered the laws of gravitation, when your great compatriot Christian Huygens laid down his wave theory of light, when Michael Faraday created the foundations of electrodynamics—the list could be continued indefinitely—"economical" points of view were certainly the last to fortify these men in their battle against traditional attitudes and overriding authorities. No: it was their unshaken faith, whether based on artistic or religious foundations, in the reality of their world-picture. In the face of this indisputable fact, we cannot brush aside the suspicion that, if the Machian principle of economy were ever to become central to the theory of knowledge, the thought processes of such leading intellects would be disturbed, the flights of their imagination would be paralyzed, and the progress of science might thus be fatally impeded. Would it not really be more "economical" to give the principle of economy a more modest place? However, you will see from my formulation of this question that I am, of course, far from wishing to disregard or dismiss a regard for "economy" in a higher sense.

Indeed, we can go a step further. Those great men did not speak about their "world-picture"; they spoke about "the world" or about

"Nature" itself. Now, is there any recognizable difference between their "world" and our "world-picture of the future"? Surely not! For the fact that no method exists for proving such a difference was made the common property of all thinkers by Immanuel Kant. The composite expression "world-picture" has now become current usage, as a precaution in order to exclude certain illusions at the outset. So, if we take pains to exercise the necessary caution, and read nothing more into the word "world" than this ideal picture of the future, we can replace the term ["world-picture"] by the word "world." In this way we can arrive at a more realistic mode of expression, which commends itself, even from the standpoint of economy, far more than Machian positivism (basically so complicated, and difficult to think through) and one which is in fact always used by physicists when they talk the language of their science.

I have just spoken of "illusions." Now it would certainly be a grave illusion on my part if I hoped to have been convincing, or even comprehensible, to all of you; and I shall take care not to fall into this illusion. Much more will certainly be thought, and written, about these basic questions, for there are many theorists, and paper is long-suffering. So we must emphasize, all the more unanimously and unreservedly, what every one of us must always recognize and cherish. That is, firstly, the need for conscientious self-criticism, together with endurance in the battle for what is seen to be right; secondly, honest respect—unshaken even by misunderstanding—for the personality of scientific opponents; and, finally, calm confidence in the power of that saying which, for over 1900 years, has taught us to distinguish false prophets from true ones by this ultimate, infallible sign: "By their fruits ye shall know them!"

2

The Guiding Principles of My Scientific

Theory of Knowledge and Its

Reception by My Contemporaries

by ERNST MACH

EDITORIAL NOTE: *Max Planck's criticisms elicited from the aging Mach—who was by this time in his seventies—the response which is reprinted here. It is a remarkable document in two respects. In the first place, it contains some classic examples of that angry and sarcastic self-justification to which Viennese intellectuals of the period —philosophers, psychoanalysts, scientists and literary men alike— were prone to resort whenever their views were subjected to critical analysis. At the same time, it presents the most concise and complete summary of Mach's mature position, covering both his "biologico-economical" analysis of cognitive processes (of which his theory of "intellectual economy" in science is a special application), and also his "sensationalist" analysis of the experiences which, in his view, are recorded in memory as "representations" and thereby become the basic "building blocks" of all scientific knowledge.*

As Mach himself makes clear, the starting point of the philosophical argument is once again Kant. But, where Planck picks on the "transcendental" element in Kant's critical philosophy and gives it a historical twist, Mach falls back into an "empiricist" posture, very close to that of David Hume—though he takes good care to insist that he had reached this position independently, before reading Hume's writings. The parallels between Mach and Hume are in fact very close. Mach's "sensations" (or Empfindungen) *are Hume's*

28

"impressions," Mach's "representations" (or Vorstellungen) *are close to Hume's "ideas"; and "concepts" (or complex ideas") are, for Mach very much as for Hume, "combinations" of these elementary ideas or "memory representations." As in the case of Bertrand Russell, who was in this respect much influenced by him, Mach was concerned with sense impressions and memory representations primarily for epistemological reasons. They are, he says, "the only immediate source of physics." By this he evidently means two things: (1) that the source of evidence to which all our claims to physical knowledge must ultimately appeal lies in those sensory impressions and memory traces; and, furthermore, (2) that the only genuinely enduring "substances" we are entitled to accept into our philosophy are permanent associations between different kinds of sense impressions, such as we discover in our experiences and formulate "economically" in so-called laws of nature. (This second point immediately calls to mind the views of Bishop Berkeley, whose influence Mach also acknowledges.)*

Over certain purely physical points, such as the validity of the atomic theory, it is tempting to share Planck's belief that Mach was allowing his skepticism to run away with him. So it is worth pointing out that, in one respect at least, Mach's theoretical foresight proved superior to that of Planck. They both discussed the relationship between mechanics and electromagnetism, which was one of the crucial issues raised as a consequence of Einstein's new relativistic theories. Planck (p. 7 above) continued to hold to the orthodox nineteenth-century expectation that, in due course, some way would be found to embrace electromagnetism within a generalized theory of mechanics, for which he invented the title of "general dynamics." Mach, on the other hand, had less of a commitment to the dynamical tradition and recognized more clearly that a major theoretical realignment was in the making, by which mechanics would eventually be subordinated to electromagnetism, rather than vice versa. This is, indeed, how things have turned out since his time. By the late 1920's, it was clear that such mechanical attributes as "impenetrability," which philosophers and physicists from 1650 on had regarded as the defining properties of "matter," were after all less fundamental than electrical and magnetic properties like "charge" and "spin."

This first round, accordingly, ends with Planck and Mach roughly level. We may feel in retrospect, today, that Planck is slightly ahead on points; but the margin is a narrow one, and there were times in

*the years between the two world wars when the verdict would have
gone the other way. For (as we shall see later) Mach's preoccupation
with the* evidential basis *of physics, and his consequent refusal to
assume any Lockean substance, or substratum, lying behind the* relationships between direct observables, *were shortly to become two of
the main themes of discussion among orthodox interpreters of
Bohr's and Heisenberg's quantum mechanics.*

IN ORDER TO describe briefly the theory of knowledge to which I
have devoted much of my life, I will begin with a statement of the
circumstances in which these principles developed.

When, at the beginning of my teaching career as a physics
lecturer in 1861, I paid close attention to the scientific works which
I had to review, I was struck by the strange way in which scientists
went about selecting the simplest, thriftiest and most efficient
method of reaching their goal. Through my dealings (in 1864) with
the political economist E. Hermann who, as befitted his calling,
sought out the ecomomic element in every type of activity, I
acquired the habit of designating the intellectual activity of the
scientist as "economic" [*wirtschaftlich*] or "economical" [*oekono-
misch*]. This can be explained by the simplest of examples. Every
abstract, comprehensive, factual statement, every replacement of a
table of figures by a formula or set of instructions (i.e., the law
governing these figures) , every explanation of a new fact by another
better known one, can be viewed as an economical achievement.
The further and more deeply one analyzes scientific methods and
their systematic, organizing, simplifying logico-mathematical structure, the more clearly one recognizes scientific activity as economical.

As a schoolboy (in 1854) , I learned about Lamarck's theories
from my esteemed schoolteacher F. X. Wessely and so was well
prepared to absorb the ideas of Darwin, published in 1859. These
played a part in my lectures at Graz as early as 1864, and they
found expression in my interpretation of the conflict between
scientific ideas as a struggle for life and as the survival of the fittest.
This view does not conflict with the economical interpretation, but
complements it, and can be combined with it to form a biologico-
economical presentation of the theory of knowledge. Expressed very

briefly, the task of scientific knowledge now appears as: *the adaptation of ideas to facts and the adaptation of ideas to one another.* Every favorable biological process is an event of self-preservation, and as such is also a process of adaptation, more economical than an event detrimental to the individual. All favorable cognitive processes are special cases, or parts, of biologically advantageous processes. For the physico-biological behavior of the higher living organisms is modified, and complemented, by the inner process of cognition or thought. The cognitive process may display the most varied qualities; we characterize it in the first place as biological, and as economical, thereby excluding aimless activity.

I have expounded these guiding principles in various writings: first in *Die Geschichte und die Wurzel des Satzes von der Erhaltung der Arbeit* [*The History and Origins of the Law of the Conservation of Energy*], 1872, with particular reference to the economy of thought; later, considering both aspects, in *Die Mechanik in ihrer Entwicklung* [*Mechanics in Its Development*], 1883, and in *Die Prinzipien der Wärmelehre* [*The Principles of the Theory of Heat*], 1896. I paid particular attention to the biological aspect in *Die Analyse der Empfindungen* [*The Analysis of Sensations*], 1886. My theory of knowledge is treated in its most mature form in *Erkenntnis und Irrtum* [*Knowledge and Error*], 1905. These writings will be cited in what follows as *C of E, M, H, A of S* and *K and E.*

Although recognition was not entirely lacking, my first publications were, very naturally, received extremely coolly and negatively by both physicists and philosophers. In fact, until the eighties of the last century, I had the feeling that I was alone, swimming against the stream, although this was in fact no longer the case. Shortly before publishing *Mechanics,* while looking for writings on similar subjects, I discovered Avenarius's *Philosophie als Denken der Welt nach dem Prinzip das Kleinsten Kraftmasses* [*Philosophy as Thinking About the World According to the Principle of Least Action*], 1876, which I quoted in the preface to my *Mechanics.* Two years after my *Analysis,* the first volume of Avenarius's *Kritik der reinen Erfahrung* [*Critique of Pure Experience*] appeared in 1888, and a few years later I was encouraged by H. Cornelius's *Psychologie als Erfahrungswissenschaft* [*Psychology as the Science of Experience*],

1897, and *Einleitung in die Philosophie* [*Introduction to Philoso-phy*], 1903, and J. Petzoldt's *Einleitung in die Philosophie der reinen Erfahrung* [*Introduction to the Philosophy of Pure Experi-ence*], 1900. Thus I realized that I was not as far away as I had thought, at least from some philosophers. Certainly the long-dead Avenarius finds more of a public, even today, in Italy, France and Russia than in his native land. Only a few years ago, I came across W. Schuppe's works, particularly his *Erkenntnistheoretischen Logik* [*Logic of the Theory of Knowledge*], 1878, and realized that this author had embarked on a similar course as early as 1870.

I found agreement among physicists much more rarely. True, I, and also Ostwald's *Energetik* [*Energetics*], had a very illustrious predecessor in W. J. M. Rankine, who had already indicated in his short essay, "Outlines of the Science of Energetics,"[1] published in 1855, the difference between an explanatory (hypothetical) physics and an abstract (descriptive) physics, and had recommended the latter as the truly scientific one, to which the first should only serve as an introductory stage. The mere fact that Rankine's arguments were, unavoidably, unknown to me when I began my work shows how little their influence had spread in space and time. When, in *C of E,* I defended the *economical representation of facts* as a means of discovering the *interdependence of phenomena* (which was at least in part a restatement of Rankine's propositions), this natu-rally passed equally unnoticed. The general astonishment which greeted Kirchhoff's definition of the task of mechanics as the "com-plete and simplest description of motions" was equally characteris-tic. The sporadic utterances which could pass for agreement with the new interpretation are mentioned in the foreword to the second impression of *C of E* (1909). Only later did we hear from Hertz that Maxwell's theory really consisted of Maxwell's equations; and only later did we hear the views of Helmholtz cited in the introduc-tion to Hertz's *Mechanik* [*Mechanics*], p. xxi. P. Duhem's *La Thé-orie Physique,* which breaks completely with the old point of view, did not appear until 1906.

In my historical studies of mechanics and heat theory, the bio-logico-economical interpretation of the cognitive process greatly

[1] *The Edinburgh New Philos. Journ.,* 2 (new series, 1855), p. 120.

facilitated my understanding of the development of science. When the struggle for self-preservation forces man into practical-economical behavior, he at first reacts quite instinctively to advantageous and disadvantageous circumstances. Only when social development, the division of labor and the creation of an artisan class compel the individual to turn his attention to intermediate means and goals for the satisfaction of his wants, does the intellect consciously come into play. Practical discomfort is then replaced by pressing intellectual discomfort. The arbitrarily selected intermediate goal is now pursued with the same zeal, and by the same means, as were formerly devoted to, say, the satisfaction of hunger. The instinctive movements of the savage, the half-consciously learned actions of the artisan, are preparations for the concepts of the scientist. The attitudes and humble everyday skills of the artisan change imperceptibly into the attitudes and devices of the physicist; and economy of action develops gradually into the *intellectual* economy of the scientist, which can also play its part in the pursuit of purely ideal goals.

I see the expression of this economy clearly in the gradual reduction of the statical laws of machines to *a single one,* viz., the principle of virtual work; in the replacement of Kepler's laws by Newton's single law, $d^2r/dt^2 = mm'/r^2$ and in the [subsequent] reduction, simplification and clarification of the laws of dynamics. I see clearly the biologico-economical adaptation of ideas, which takes place by the principles of continuity (permanence) and of adequate definition and splits the concept "heat" into the two concepts "temperature" and "quantity of heat"; and I see how the concept "quantity of heat" leads on to "latent heat," and to the concepts of "energy" and "entropy." But this is matter for books, and not a subject for an essay.

The biologico-economical viewpoint may be arbitrary, limited and one-sided, perhaps even inappropriate, but I cannot believe that it is false or unproductive. Petzoldt chooses to speak of "stability" rather than "economy": I prefer "economy," because it was the analogy with everyday life that first led me to an understanding of the metamorphoses of science. Other points of view will be discussed later.

To show what interpretation my theory of knowledge receives

from eminent modern physicists, I must ask the reader to turn, if possible, to M. Planck's "The Unity of the Physical World-Picture" (Leipzig, 1909) [2] as I have to take issue with this 38-page essay. I will discuss its contents purely objectively, without reacting to, let alone imitating, its form—"*Le style, c'est l'homme*."

Planck distinguishes on p. 4 [pp. 3–4] between two methods of operation in physics, roughly in Rankine's sense: one proceeding from observed individual phenomena to daring generalizations and *explanations,* the other aiming at sober *descriptions.* As examples of the former, he mentions Thales's water theory, Ostwald's energetics, and Hertz's "straightest path"; as a representative of the latter he cites Kirchhoff. Now, I am glad that energetics is credited with a certain "impetus," although it had had "not the slightest" success in Lübeck; but I can only allocate energetics to Rankine's second method, likewise Hertz's ideas about the straightest path. And if one studies Kirchhoff's "complete and simplest description" in detail, it is not only descriptive but leaves no room for explanations. For "once a fact is fully known in all its aspects, it is thereby explained and the task of science is completed" (J. R. Mayer). Kirchhoff, for his part, certainly did not see himself as in opposition to any second method. According to Planck, research cannot dispense with either of the two methods; I certainly consider Kirchhoff's to be the right one, without denying the historically tested utility of the other.

On p. 5 (*Phys. Zeitschr.,* 10 [1909], 62) [above, p. 4] P. asks how the physical world-picture produced by the application of these two methods is made up. "Is it merely a convenient but basically arbitrary intellectual concept, or is one driven to the opposite interpretation, namely, that it reflects real natural events which are quite independent of us?" Here I can find no irreconcilable contradiction. It must be convenient, in order to guide us; how else could we make use of it? It must also be dependent on individuality, and therefore to some extent arbitrary. This is shown by comparing Newton's optics with Huygens's, Biot's with that of Young and Fresnel, or Lagrange's mechanics with that of Poinsot and Hertz. What could prevent scientists from paying particular

[2] This journal [*Phys. Zeitschr.*], 10 (1909), 62.

attention to different aspects of the facts? The decree of a sufficiently eminent physicist? But, thanks to a changing succession of scientists, the human, socially maintained world-picture will naturally become a progressively purer expression of the facts, ever more independent of individuality. In general, the environment as well as the observer finds expression in every observation and every opinion.

Pages 6 and 7 (*PZ* 63) [pp. 5–6] contain known historical facts about which there is little to be said.

Page 8 (*PZ* 64) [p. 7] discusses the unification of the physical system, to which nobody would object—least of all an exponent of intellectual economy, even if this unification is only a provisional, hypothetico-fictitious[3] one. However, I believe that electrodynamics—or let us say Lorentz's theory—is much more likely, as W. Wien argues, to absorb mechanics as a special case than the other way round.

I also agree in essentials with the views expressed on pp. 10–c. 29 (*PZ* 64–71) [pp. 8–21] concerning the first and second laws of thermodynamics, in particular, the important distinction between reversible and irreversible events. For even if these laws did happen to be discovered in connection with practical-economical questions, intellectual economy is in no way restricted or confined in its aims to the examination of human-practical-economical needs.

Still, I cannot conceal my dislike for hypothetico-fictitious physics. That is the reason for my personal opinion about Boltzmann's probability investigations into the second law, based on the kinetic theory of gases. Even if Boltzmann found that events in conformity with the second law are very probable, while those contrary to it are only very improbable, I cannot accept that behavior in accordance with this law has thereby been demonstrated. And I cannot think it right for P. to accept the first part, without observing the second (p. 24, *PZ* 72) [p. 16] since the two halves of the inference cannot be separated. And how could an absolutely conservative system of elastic atoms be prevailed upon to behave like a system tending toward a final state, even by the most skillful mathematical considerations, which cannot have any real influence on it? See *H* (2nd ed.), p. 364, and also Seeliger *Über die Anwendung der Natur-*

---

[3] I have borrowed the expression *fiktiv* ["fictitious"] from H. Driesch.

gesetze auf das Universum ["On the Application of Laws of Nature to the Universe"], *München-Akad.* (May 1, 1909), p. 20. On p. 29 (*PZ* 72) [p. 21] P. asserts that sense impressions cannot be ignored as the source of our experience, but that the colorless kinetic world-picture is preferable because of its unity. This world-picture is said (p. 31, *PZ* 72) [p. 23] to be not only independent of the individual, but also valid for all times and peoples, and even for the quite differently organized inhabitants of Mars. Anyone who does not recognize this is said to cut himself off from the physicist's mode of thinking. On p. 34 (*PZ* 73) [p. 24] we find the statement that atoms are no less real than heavenly bodies, and that the fact that one hydrogen atom weighs $1.6 \times 10^{-24}g$ is just as certain as that the moon weighs $7 \times 10^{25}g$. Incidentally, we find a similar observation in H. A. Lorentz, the well-known founder of the modern theory of electrons.

I, too, regard sense impressions as the source of all experience, but I do not believe that they should be consigned to oblivion again as soon as physical concepts have been formed; I ascribe a higher value to them, as a link between physics and the other sciences. I have attempted elsewhere to show how a unified physics can gradually be built up without artificial hypotheses[4]—although not in a day.

This preoccupation with a physics valid for all times and peoples (including Martians), at a time when many everyday physical questions still puzzle us, seems to me highly premature, and indeed almost ludicrous. But this question, too, I answered years ago. All living creatures who may study physics in the future will be obliged, like us, to provide for their own survival and therefore to pay attention to whatever in nature is economically important and permanent for them; and this would give them a point of contact with our physics, if by some miracle it were available to them.[5] Indeed, I have no doubt that if, somewhere in the universe, a creature organized like ourselves could make observations before the beginning or after the end of the earth, it would perceive a universe working similarly to that which we ourselves describe. I can attribute only this hypothetical meaning to Planck's question

[4] "Über das Prinzip der Vergleichungen in der Physik," *Populäre Vorlesungen* (3rd ed., 1903), p. 263.

[5] *K and E* (2nd ed., 1906), p. 149.

on p. 32 (*PZ* 73) [p. 23]. According to my biologico-economical interpretation, this belief is not unfounded, and certainly does not depend on the quality of sensations. As for the "reality" of atoms: I have no doubt that, if atomic theory corresponds to the reality given by the senses, the conclusions drawn from it will also bear some relation to the facts—though what relation remains unclear. The distance from the glass of the first dark ring in reflected light corresponds to one-half of the period of Newton's "fits" [of easy reflection and refraction], but to one-quarter of Young and Fresnel's "wavelength." The findings of atomic theory, likewise, can undergo a variety of convenient reinterpretations, even if we are in no great hurry to take them for realities. So all honor to the beliefs of physicists! But I cannot share them myself.

If Planck's lecture had ended on p. 32 (*PZ* 73) [p. 23], I would have had no cause to discuss it. But at this point there begins a polemical passage explicitly directed against me, which made me realize that in the earlier part too there are recognizable shafts which passed me by without wounding me, but which were clearly intended for me or my kind. This is why I have discussed the first part also. These final polemics compel me to utter a few words of rebuttal, on account of their unusual form, their complete ignorance of the matter in dispute, and their strange conclusion. The following section of this essay will be devoted to correcting Planck's survey of my allegedly perverse interpretation of sense impressions.

As the reader will have remarked, the biologico-economical interpretation of the cognitive process can perfectly well co-exist on peaceable, and indeed on friendly, terms with that of present-day physics. The only real point of difference which has so far come to light concerns the belief in the reality of atoms. Here again, Planck can hardly find words degrading enough for such wrongheadedness. Anyone who enjoys psychological conjectures must read his lecture for himself, and is welcome to do so. After exhorting the reader, with Christian charity, to respect his opponent, P. brands me, in the well-known biblical words, as a "false prophet." It appears that physicists are on the way to founding a church; they are already using a church's traditional weapons. To this I answer simply: "If belief in the reality of atoms is so important to you, I cut myself off from the physicist's mode of thinking (p. 31, *PZ* 72) [p. 23], I do

not wish to be a true physicist (p. 33, *PZ* 73) [p. 24], I renounce all
scientific respect (p. 35, *PZ* 74) [p. 25]—in short: I decline with
thanks the communion of the faithful. I prefer freedom of thought."

I must recall one more influence which helped to determine the
development of my ideas. Chronologically, it was the first, but for
various reasons I mention it last. In 1853, in my early youth, my
naïve-realistic view of the world was deeply shaken by Kant's
Prolegomena. A year or two later, I instinctively recognized that the
"thing-in-itself" was a mere illusion and returned to Berkeley's
standpoint (which is latent in Kant). But this idealistic mood
accorded ill with the study of physics. My discomfort was increased
by familiarity with Herbart's mathematical psychology, and with
Fechner's psychophysics, in which acceptable and unacceptable
strands were closely interwoven. After completing my university
studies, I had the ill (or good) fortune not to be in a position to
engage in physical researches, so that I was forced into the field of
sensory physiology. There, where I could observe my own sense
impressions, and also their dependence on the environment, I
believe that I arrived at a natural interpretation of the world, free
of speculative-metaphysical additions. The distaste for metaphysics
implanted by Kant and by the analyses of Herbart and Fechner led
me back to a position close to that of Hume.[6]

We find ourselves feeling, thinking and acting in space, along
with inorganic and organic objects, plants, animals and men. I
distinguish my own body from the similar bodies of other men by
special peculiarities of behavior. Observation of other men leads
me, by irresistible analogy, to assume that they make similar
observations to mine; that their bodies bear the same special
relationship to them that mine bears to me; and that they experience through their bodies the same particular feelings, wishes and
actions as I do through mine. Their conduct also leads me to

---

[6] I was not directly influenced by Hume, whose work I did not know, but his
younger contemporary Lichtenberg may have affected me. I certainly remember
the strong impression made on me by his "It thinks." I did not become acquainted with Hume's *Enquiry Concerning Human Understanding* (in Kirch-
mann's translation) until the late 1880's, or with his much more important
Treatise on Human Nature until 1907–8. Today I view the metaphysics-free position as a product of general cultural development. See also "Sur le rapport de la
physique avec la psychologie," Binet, *L'Année psychologique,* 12 (1906), 303–318.

suppose that my body and other objects are as directly "given" to them as their bodies and other objects are to me; but that my memories, wishes, etc., can only be inferred by them, as theirs can by me. That which is given to all in common we call the "physical"; that which is directly given only to one, and can only be inferred by others, we call the "psychical." That which is given only to one can also be called the "ego" [*Ich*].

The simplest experiences suffice to support the hypotheses of a world common to all, and of other egos besides one's own; and these hypotheses prove equally advantageous for both theoretial and practical conduct. As our experience becomes progressively more detailed, howeoer, it teaches us that the world is not as directly given to us as it at first appeared to be. In order to see an object, we require the presence of another, luminescent one; in order to hear an object, we require it to be vibrated, and these vibrations must reach our ears. Furthermore, the receiving eye and ear must be healthy and functioning normally. Even the man in the street knows how external circumstances and sense organs affect our impressions of the world, so that it appears somewhat different to each one of us. Scientific experience confirms this, and teaches us further that sensation (perception) is determined by the final link in a chain reaching from the environment to the central organ of sense; in exceptional cases, it can occur spontaneously, without external stimulus, in the form of a hallucination. In this case, correction by other senses or other persons is required, if the resulting judgement is to have scientific, and therefore social, value. Placing too great an importance on these exceptional cases can easily lead to monstrous systems of idealism, or even solipsism.

It would be most strange if the very refinement of experience were to carry it aloft, high above the world, leaving nothing of the world itself but inaccessible phantoms.[7] We can in fact escape this disquieting possibility, by examining it more closely. Everything that we see, hear, touch, etc., is related to whatever else we see, hear, touch, etc.; but also to whatever can be established about our own bodies, by a coarser or finer sensory examination. This is true, not only of perceptions in general, but also—if we divide our impres-

7 *L'Année psychologique,* 12 (1906) , 307.

sions into the simplest qualitative elements: colors, tones, pressures, etc.—of these elements themselves. Let us call *ABCDE* . . . the elementary sensory components of the environment, *L* the limits between our bodies and the environment, and *KLMN* . . . the elementary sensory components which we find enclosed by the surface, *L*. Then, every element of the first group, e.g., *A* (the green of a leaf) is related to other elements of the same group, e.g., *B* (sunlight containing green) but also to elements of the second group, e.g., *K* (openness of eyes) and *N* (sensitivity of retina). These established facts, which are quite independent of any particular theory, cannot and must not be overlooked by any sound theory of knowledge. Everyone will recognize the relationships within the first group as *physical,* and the quite different type of relationships crossing the limits, *L,* as *psychological.*[8]

The foregoing passage suffices to show how much Planck's various misgivings about sense impressions are worth. The observed interdependence of *ABCDE* . . . is not arbitrary: it is *physical* or, if you like, *"real."* (p. 5, PZ 63.) [p. 4] Only the *physiological* depends on the individuality of the body; it is not "lawless," but can be controlled or eliminated, like the influence of an individual galvanometer, thermometer, etc. This also disposes of P's remarks about reality on p. 35 (*PZ* 74) [p. 25]. Far from regretting that we cannot exclude sense impressions (p. 29, *PZ* 72) [p. 21], we should rather value them as the only immediate source of physics, and we should not consign them to oblivion immediately after use. For, if the origin of the concept "force" goes back to "a sense of muscular strain" (p. 7, *PZ* 63) [p. 6], this shows that, whenever and wherever muscular strain does or could come into play, we must assume that anything mobile will accelerate, as Galileo proved in the case of a heavy body.[9] Highly significant abstractions can thus be based on a sensation. There can, in my view, be no question of interpreting sensations in a purely subjective way, as P. seems to assume on p. 33 (*PZ* 73) [p. 24]. I do not know if "Machian positivism—so difficult to think through" (p. 37, *PZ* 75) [p. 27] still lacks the key to its completely consistent interpretation, which

---

[8] *K and E* (2nd ed.) , p. 10.
[9] *K and E,* p. 140.

P. seems to possess on p. 35 *(PZ 74)* [p. 26]; I shall, of course, be grateful for any assistance.

I may add that on p. 34 *(PZ 74)* [p. 25] P. does not do my "positivism" justice when he views it as a reaction against the failures of atomistic speculations. Even if the physical world-picture of kinetic theory, which (without wishing to degrade it) I regard as merely hypothetical, could "explain" all physical phenomena, I would not consider the manifold of the world as completely exhausted; to my mind, *Matter, Time* and *Space* are also still problems toward which physicists (Lorentz, Einstein, Minkowski) are gradually moving. Physics is not the whole universe; there is *biology,* too, which forms an equally essential part of the world-picture. The elements *ABCDE* . . . can be classified as *sensations* only in their relation to *KLMN* . . . ; in their interrelations, *ABCDE* . . . are *physical characteristics.* The chief and most general task of natural science is to clarify this interrelation. Sensations leave memory traces (representations) of sensory experiences, whether these consist of elements, or of more or less complex associations of elements. Reproductions of sensory experiences by memories (representations) are the first building blocks of science. As these representations (or ideas) adapt themselves to experiences, our knowledge of the environment grows, and so also does our practical and intellectual use of this knowledge. *Representations* are not *qualitatively* new elements as compared with impressions. But representations are linked to stimulations of the central organ [of sense], impressions to stimulations of a *sensory receptor.* One cannot initiate anything in the environment by means of an imaginary shining, flickering, burning flame, but a *sensed* shining, flickering, burning flame is bound *to be a flame,* with which one can boil water. Thus, sensations belong to both physical and psychical worlds, representations only to the latter.

I hope that the relationship between my views and Planck's has been made sufficiently clear. I shall add only a few remarks to indicate more precisely the basis of my theory of knowledge.

Anything which *exists unconditionally* we call "substance." I can see an object if I look at it, I can feel it if I touch it. I can see it without feeling it, and vice versa. As a rule, however, visibility and tangibility are linked. Although the emergence of the elements of this complex takes place only on certain conditions, these are so familiar to us that we hardly notice them. We regard an object as being always present, whether or not it is sensible at the time. We are accustomed to regarding the object as existing unconditionally, although *there is no such thing as unconditional existence*.[10]

The sight of an object can immediately call up the whole complex, which can be advantageous, but can also be misleading, if for example I have apprehended a purely optical image. Thus, we have every reason to distinguish a thing (a whole complex of elements) from its appearance (a part of the complex). However, to extrapolate this experience beyond the proper limits of experience, and to assume the existence of a "thing-in-itself," has no intelligible meaning.

We have become accustomed to regarding an object as existing permanently. By omitting now this, now that sensory element, without the remainder ceasing to represent and call up the object, we can easily jump to the conclusion that, even if we omitted all the elements, there would always be something left. We imagine an extrasensory *group* of elements, a *carrier* of qualities, a *substance* of the object, in the philosophical sense. This idea has no foundation in the elements which we have called *ABCDE* . . . ; it is purely a product of creative fantasy.

The physicist means something quite different by "substance" or "quantity." An object has a certain weight. If one divides it and weighs all the parts separately, the sum of the weights will be equal to the original weight. The same applies to the volumes of the object and its parts, of their heat capacities, etc. Comparable measurements which, on certain conditions, always yield a constant sum, are physical entities, *substances,* quantities.[11]

In the simplest cases, the observed interrelations of the elements *ABCDE* . . . are reproduced by sensory representations and retained in the memory as the building blocks of a rudimentary natural science. If several or many such building blocks can be combined to produce a larger component, in the form of a *concept,*

[10] *A of S* (1886) , pp. 154–157; (5th ed., 1906) , pp. 268 ff.

[11] *H* (2nd ed., 1900) , pp. 422 ff. It is also indicated there that it makes little difference to the mathematician whether a sum is fixed as constant, or whether the solution of further equations is called for.

this will be advantageous. Such a concept is no more than the ability, designated and stimulated by the word, to recall the single experiences from which the concept was gradually formed. A higher concept can contain other concepts (as characteristics) ; but such a concept, if it is to have any scientific meaning, will also be based on sensory experiences of the elements *ABCDE . . . P*. seems to admit this, when he says on p. 34 *(PZ 73)* [p. 24]: "A single glance into a precision laboratory shows us how many experiences and a abstractions are comprised in one such measurement (weighing)." Yes, indeed: when applied to a concrete example, the most abstract concepts are rapidly reduced to the elements from which the theory was built up. The concept must, of course, have contained the elements found in it: these elements may, in fact, be more important than the components interpolated by the imagination.

I have explained and demonstrated elsewhere[12] that our physical concepts, however close they come to the facts, must not be regarded as a complete and final expression of these facts. Those concepts which are parts of a continuum of concepts—i.e., mathematical concepts—are of particular importance.[13] The *permanence of the linking of reactions* described by *physical laws* is the *highest substantiality* which science has so far discovered, more permanent than anything hitherto known as "substance." I do not propose to investigate the motives for P.'s attacks on my theory of knowledge, or the object of these attacks. Others may judge whether he was right, and whether my views are really in such glaring contradiction to any viable physics. P. thinks that I am presumptuous in attaching such importance to intellectual economy. But was he not guilty of (shall we say?) temerity in attacking, at the first disagreeable or uncongenial impression, something he was quite ignorant about, and which was alien to the direction and manner of his thinking? I consider it no misfortune that ideas based on facts develop differently in different minds—on the contrary! Nor do I take contradiction tragically; it often shines like a torch into the mental worlds of others, and also into one's own. But one should first make some attempt to understand one's opponent.

12 *K and E,* p. 141.
13 *K and E,* p. 136; see also note 1, p. 606, col. 1 [p. 42] of this essay.

3

On Mach's Theory of
Physical Knowledge: A Reply

by MAX PLANCK

EDITORIAL NOTE: *Max Planck now returned to the attack, this time more directly* ad hominem. *Mach's evolutionary or "biologico-economical" approach—he argues—is essentially vague, and the simplicity of his phrase "intellectual economy" is deceptive. For the aim of an intellectual strategy in physics is not to achieve biologically advantageous results, nor, strictly speaking, to achieve economically advantageous results either: it is to reap intellectual advantages, whose analogies with biology and economics are at best partial and far-fetched. No doubt—he comments—Mach can stretch his definition of "intellectual economy" to embrace, also, the unity and rationality of a coherent and well-established world-picture, but to do this will be arbitrary and unhelpful. For instance, is atomism to be regarded as a legitimate theoretical simplification (and so "good") or as a needless multiplication of entities (and so "bad")? For all that one can see, the idea of intellectual economy could be extended, at choice, to defend either of these judgments.*

On the epistemological front, the differences between Mach and Planck remain, at the end of the exchange, in deadlock. In the subsequent essays we shall see their successors oscillating between the two extremes they have defined. On the one hand, there are those like the mature Einstein, who share Planck's revised Kantianism, recognizing that mathematical theories are in themselves "free products of the creative intellect," but having confidence that such theories can be made progressively less arbitrary and given a progressively more general and universal interpretation as physics. On

44

the other hand, there are those who follow Mach in limiting the claims of physics to the establishment of constant relations between direct observables. Under the positivistic shadow of the Vienna Circle—as we shall see—Mach's "phenomenalist" strategy achieved something of a dominance in the heyday of quantum mechanics, when it appeared that Heisenberg's Uncertainty Relation set an inescapable limit to physical observation. But those with a more "transcendental" turn of mind continued, like Planck, to defend the legitimacy of more imaginative theoretical constructions, which might be capable of carrying Planck's process of "generalization and universalization" beyond the furthest points that quantum mechanics could reach.

IN A GENERAL lecture on physics which I gave two years ago at Leiden,[1] I had occasion to criticize some points in Mach's theory of knowledge. My remarks met with a certain interest and some direct agreement even in circles which are remote from physics, particularly among well-known exponents of transcendental philosophy; but they encountered, as was to be expected, a more or less harsh rejection from members of Mach's school.

Until now, I had no intention of returning to this subject, as I for my part had nothing new to say about it, and I also felt that I had expressed my opinion on its most important points sufficiently clearly. But I have begun to doubt this since the appearance of an article by Ernst Mach[2] entitled: "The Guiding Principles of My Scientific Theory of Knowledge and Its Reception by My Contemporaries," which also appeared in this periodical.[3] In this, Mach not only declares that his theory of knowledge is not disproved, but also fails to take my criticisms seriously, and finally goes so far as to deny my competence to make any contribution to the physical theory of knowledge.

Although it must appear somewhat remarkable that Mach has not found a worthier adversary—after all, I am not his only

---

1 M. Planck, *The Unity of the Physical World-Picture* (Leipzig: S. Hirzel, 1909). This periodical [*Phys. Zeitschr.*], 10 (1909), 62 [pp. 3–27 above].

2 E. Mach, *Scientia, International Periodical for Scientific Synthesis*, 7 (1910), 14, 225.

3 E. Mach, this periodical [*Phys. Zeitschr.*], 11 (1910), 599 [pp. 30–43 above].

contemporary—I feel compelled by this curious choice to formulate my attitude toward Mach's theory of knowledge rather more clearly than hitherto seemed called for. It should soon become apparent that my critics have treated the matter rather too lightly.

I believe that I am entitled to express an opinion about Mach's theory of physical knowledge on the grounds that I have been concerned with this theory for years. During my Kiel period (1885–89) I was one of the staunchest supporters of Mach's philosophy, which, I freely acknowledge, had a strong influence on my thinking as a physicist. But I later abandoned it, chiefly because I came to realize that Mach's natural philosophy was not capable of fulfilling the brilliant promise which attracted most of its supporters: viz., the elimination of all metaphysical elements from the physical theory of knowledge. Proof of this assertion is implicit in the contents of my Leiden lecture, but I will now attempt to make it even clearer. It will be best to start with the exposition of his theory which Mach himself gave in the last-named publication.

In his opening pages Mach explains once again, quite clearly and convincingly, the well-known argument which led him to the belief that knowledge of nature is fundamentally biologico-economical. But anyone who believes that this expresses the whole substance of Mach's theory, and that the subsequent criticism of my Leiden lecture results simply from the logical application of that point of view, is very much mistaken. The main point is yet to come, and consists of a tacit but significant shift in the concepts previously established.

Thus he states at the beginning of his discussion of my thermodynamic arguments that "intellectual economy is in no way restricted or confined in its aims to the examination of human-practical-economical needs." This is something very different from what was stated earlier. Intellectual economy is not confined in its aims to human-practical needs! To what other needs then? The aims of intellectual economy are, and must be, derived from the practical aspects of human life. A few pages earlier, Mach actually emphasized: "All favorable cognitive processes are special cases, or parts, of biologically advantageous processes." Does intellectual economy serve other purposes besides the furthering of human knowledge? In vain do we seek an answer to this question. I therefore venture to state that, as a result of this unsupported generalization, the concept of economy loses its original meaning and is transformed into a metaphysical concept.

In short, the situation is as follows. Scientific physics developed, as is universally acknowledged, from practical human needs; therefore, Mach concludes, physical knowledge is fundamentally economical in nature. Mach adheres to this last statement throughout all that follows. After it has become apparent that, as scientific physics in fact develops, it continually sheds its practical-human character (as cannot really be denied), he goes on to conclude, not that the economical interpretation is inadequate, but that intellectual economy is not tied to a human-practical point of view. I believe this to be a brief summary of the basis of Mach's theory of knowledge.

Now, we cannot prevent anyone from defining a concept as he pleases. But it really will not do, first, to play the principle of economy as a trump card against metaphysics, by express reference to its human-practical meaning, and later, when it no longer quite meets the case, to deny the human-practical aspect of economy with equal emphasis. Using this flexible concept of economy, one can of course do anything, or rather one can do absolutely nothing precise. In any case, when he makes use of this extended definition of economy, Mach can no longer claim that by introducing this concept he has liberated physical knowledge from all metaphysical elements—at least, not as long as he uses his own definition of metaphysical concepts, as those of which one has forgotten how one reached them.

The foregoing considerations were in my mind when, in my Leiden lecture, I made the remark which has been so sharply attacked: that Mach's theory of knowledge, if pursued logically, displays no inner contradiction, but that basically it has only a formalistic meaning, since it lacks the outstanding characteristic of all scientific research—the demand for a *constant* world-picture.

Now, F. W. Adler[4] claims to have defeated me decisively when he cites a passage (in fact well known to me) from Mach's *Principles*

4 Friedrich W. Adler, "The Unity of the Physical World-Picture," *Naturwissenschaftliche Wochenscrift,* 8 (1909), 52—an essay whose objective tone is agreeably different from the highly personal flavor of Mach's article.

of the Theory of Heat, in which a world-picture of the greatest possible *stability* is stated to be the aim of scientific economy. I entirely agree with this; but what I disputed, and still dispute, is the statement that stability of the world-picture is demanded by Mach's intellectual economy. Mach (it is true) attempts to weaken the distinction between stability and economy as far as possible. "Petzoldt chooses to speak of 'stability' rather than 'economy': I prefer 'economy.'" As if the use of one expression in place of the other were simply a minor matter of taste! In reality, these two concepts are, of course, worlds apart. For economy is inseparable from expediency, whereas the concept of stability has absolutely nothing to do with expediency. One might just as well, conversely, present variability (i.e., the possibility of development) as a demand of economy. Here, too, it is clear that, behind the officially unchanging phrases, the concepts are gradually shifted until the desired result can be pronounced.

I am not inclined to pursue this discussion further. For I cannot hope to convince my adversaries; on the contrary, I must be prepared to be reproached for having again misunderstood everything. So I will calmly let the approaching flood flow over me, and wait until something factually new appears.

But who is to give the final verdict in this argument? "By their fruits ye shall know them!" I am sorry, but I really am unable to suggest a higher court of appeal than this. Strangely enough, Mach is displeased with this judgment, by which I hoped to be peacefully and amicably reconciled with him; he suspects it of masking disguised Christianity. But there is no help for it—Mach and his theory of knowledge will have to bow to this judgment, like so many theories before him, even though it is in the Bible. So let us try the fruits; several lie before us on either side.

Mach says that he is able to agree in general with my discussion of the laws of thermodynamics. I regret that I cannot say the same of his work on the principles of the theory of heat,[5] and I am surprised that he did not notice the criticism of it in my arguments.

[5] E. Mach, *Die Prizipien der Wärmelehre, historisch-kritisch entwickelt* [*The Principles of the Theory of Heat, Developed Historically and Critically*] (Leipzig: J. A. Barth, 1896; 2nd ed., 1900) . The page references which follow apply to both editions.

I am compelled to state here, even more clearly, that a study of this work can, at best, give the reader only a superficial view of the principles of heat theory.

It is true that this book contains frequent references to the *perpetuum mobile,* but no particular physical meaning is attached to this term. For a *perpetuum mobile* of the first kind (the production of energy from nothing) is constantly confused with a *perpetuum mobile* of the second kind (uncompensated production of energy from heat). For instance, when Mach says: "The law of the impossibility of perpetual motion can be recognized, most clearly and easily, in the purely mechanical field, where it in fact first took root" (p. 318), he is no doubt thinking of a *perpetuum mobile* of the first kind. On the other hand, when he says: "A reversible cycle produces the maximum amount of energy which can correspond to the transfer of a precise amount of heat from a higher to a lower temperature. This maximum is the same for all materials, since otherwise perpetual motion would be possible" (p. 302), we must assume, if this statement is to have any meaning, that he is thinking of a *perpetuum mobile* of the second kind. The fact that the two laws, stating the impossibility of the two kinds of *perpetuum mobile,* are totally different—that, for instance, the first law can be reversed (energy cannot be destroyed) but the second cannot (the uncompensated production of heat from energy is by no means impossible); that the energy principle (the first proposition) is based on the first law, while the Carnot-Clausius principle (the second proposition) is based on the second law; that the second law is completely equivalent to Clausius's well-known law about the transfer of heat from a lower to a higher temperature;[6] that this law assumes the existence of irreversible processes; that no proof can be found for the Carnot-Clausius principle without assuming the existence of irreversible processes—there is not a single syllable in Mach's book about any of these facts, or about much else that is equally important; although, as I must emphasize, at the time of writing (1896) the facts of the case had been made perfectly clear, forty years earlier, by the works of R. Clausius and W. Thomson.

6 Thus Adler is mistaken in thinking that Clausius's law contains no anthropomorphous elements.

Instead, he makes elaborate observations about the analogy between heat and electricity; in particular, he argues that there are only "purely historical and quite incidental formal and conventional reasons" for not viewing electricity (like heat) as motion; that, in fact, if Riess's electrical air thermometer had been invented earlier than Coulomb's torsion balance, electricity would very probably be viewed today as a kind of motion (p. 323). As if Riess's air thermometer and Coulomb's balance were the only instuments through which we know anything about electricity! As if Faraday, Feddersen and Hertz had not conducted certain experiments with electricity, which show that Mach's ostentatious analogy is completely external and formal, since according to them electricity, unlike heat, possesses inertia.

With reference to the absolute zero of temperature, he remarks: "In fact, it has been assumed that a cooling below this temperature is inconceivable, that a body of −273°C contains no thermal energy etc. Nevertheless, I believe that these conclusions are based on inadmissibly bold extrapolation" (p. 341). Belief in a physical law can be neither enforced nor forbidden. But the fact that Mach finds Carnot's principle compatible with this view, as the sentences show, throws sufficient light on his interpretation of the meaning of Carnot's principle.

Mach's *Mechanics*,[7] which has had a beneficial influence (as I particularly emphasized in my Leiden lecture) by stimulating historical interest and counterbalancing a certain dogmatism, is on a higher level than his *Principles of the Theory of Heat*. But I have not succeeded in discovering a tangible physical result, a physical law, or even an opinion of value to physical research, which one could designate as typical of Mach's biologico-economical theory of knowledge. On the contrary: when Mach attempts to advance independently on the basis of his theory of knowledge, he often goes astray.

This applies to Mach's hotly defended but physically quite useless idea that the relativity of all translational motions has a counter-

---

[7] E. Mach, *Die Mechanik in ihrer Entwicklung, historisch-kritisch dargestellt* [*Mechanics in Its Development, Presented Historically and Critically*] (Leipzig: F. A. Brockhaus, 1883).

part in the relativity of all rotational motions—e.g., that we cannot determine, in principle, whether a sky of fixed stars rotates around the static earth or whether the earth rotates against a static sky of fixed stars. The general and simple statement that, in nature, the angular velocity of an infinitely distant body around an axis with a finite location cannot possibly have a finite value is, for Mach, either incorrect or inapplicable. For Mach's mechanics, the one is as bad as the other.

It would take too long to describe, in detail, the erroneous physical concepts produced by this inadmissible transference of the law of relativity of rotational motions from kinematics to mechanics. Also of relevance is the fact that Mach's theories cannot possibly do justice to the tremendous advance connected with the introduction of Copernican cosmology. This fact alone would suffice to put Mach's theory of knowledge in a doubtful light.

So there is not much to be made of the "fruits" for the present. But perhaps in the future? I am always ready to be enlightened by facts. Mach doubts the reducibility of the second law to probability, he does not believe in the reality of atoms. Very well: perhaps he or one of his disciples will one day develop another theory more effective than the present one. We must wait and see.

However, we must not assume that these opinions of Mach's really represent strict inferences from his theory of knowledge. Far from it! Such a formalistic theory, as I stressed earlier, can have no definite physical result, either true or false. It would not surprise me if, one day, a member of Mach's school came up with the great discovery that the probability hypothesis, or the reality of atoms, is in fact a consequence of scientific economy. Then everything would be perfectly in order, atomism would be saved, and there would be the particular advantage that everyone could use the word "economy" to mean whatever he liked.

In spite of these alluring prospects, I consider that we should give the term "economy" a real meaning, and thus allow it to retain its human-practical significance. This is important enough, even for pure science. For, just as the first beginnings of physics, and also of every other natural science, lie in the practical field, so today scientific physics still receives its greatest stimulus, as well as its most powerful support, from the needs of practical life. That is why it is in the interests of science to maintain and develop a close contact with technology.

But even in its widest sense the principle of economy is not capable of leading the way for physical research, for the simple reason that one can never tell in advance from which point of view economy will appear most valuable and durable. So a physicist who wishes to advance his science must be a realist, not an economist— that is, he must first and foremost seek among varying phenomena whatever is lasting and eternal, and try to bring it to light. Intellectual economy will serve him as a means, but not as an end. This has always been the case and—in spite of E. Mach and his so-called anti-metaphysics—will no doubt always remain the case.

4

Anthropomorphism and Physics

by T. PERCY NUNN

EDITORIAL NOTE: *Despite the disruptions caused by World War I, the fifteen years following 1911 saw striking developments in both physics and philosophy. Einstein's two theories of relativity attracted widespread attention, particularly when a solar eclipse immediately after the war provided an opportunity to check the differing predictions obtained on Newtonian and relativistic principles for the deflection of light from a star passing very close to the edge of the sun. Meanwhile, Niels Bohr's explanation of the hydrogen spectrum provided the first spectacular demonstration of the power of the new quantum theory of sub-atomic structure, but did so only at a price, since the assumptions that Bohr was compelled to make about, for example, the stability of the electronic orbits seemed, for the time being, both arbitrary and paradoxical.*

Dr. Nunn's essay, originally delivered as the annual Henriette Hertz lecture at the British Academy, London, in December, 1926, is of special interest since it captures admirably the state of opinion in the philosophy of physical science at the moment of emergence of the new systems of wave mechanics and quantum mechanics. Dr. Nunn refers to these new theories in his closing pages, in passages added to his original lecture, but his main argument must be considered without reference to them and represents rather an attempt to find a middle way between the opposing positions put forward earlier by Planck and Mach.

As Dr. Nunn rightly emphasizes, the philosophical presuppositions of Einstein's theories had been initially misunderstood. Far from sharing Leibniz's "relational" analysis of spatial concepts, as

*referring only to the "orders of co-existence and succession" of real,
material things, Einstein attributed a more profound "reality" to
the composite entity he called "space-time" than he did to matter
itself: by the word "matter" he designated simply the local distor-
tions of the "space-time metric" that manifested themselves through
force fields, inertia and other physical effects. Philosophically speaking, therefore, Einstein was talking the language of an extreme
"realism," even though with Kantian overtones.*

*The aim of Dr. Nunn's essay is to do justice to the reasons which
had prompted Einstein to claim for the space-time metric an objectivity and "independence from anthropomorphous elements" of
the kind Planck had insisted on, while yet giving proper weight to
Mach's emphasis on the evidential primacy of* Empfindungen *or, in
Dr. Nunn's word, "sensa." The result is a system highly reminiscent
of Kant. Objectivity lies, for Dr. Nunn, in the schema by which
"sensa" (or "phenomena") are ordered, within a Planckian "unified
world-picture": it is (so to say) the "common order of sensibilia."
At the same time, it is a system from which the earlier empiricist
contrast between primary and secondary qualities has been eliminated and in which colors, scents and the like have as much claim
to permanent existence—through their order of interrelatedness—as
shapes, sizes and velocities.*

*This compromise may strike a reader nowadays as more of a
tour de force than anything solid, but it has several genuine merits.
For it shows how radical were the reappraisals brought about by the
changes in physical theory between 1910 and 1925; it reminds us
how closely, from the time of Galileo if not of Democritus, the problem of physical reality had been related to the philosophical problem of perception; and it keeps well in view the tension between
the Kantian strains in Einstein's theories and the Humean commit-
ments that Mach's example had transmitted to the Vienna Circle
and to the founders of quantum mechanics.*

"ANTHROPOMORPHISM" MEANT originally the attribution of the human shape to God, and, as theologians have remarked, is always
connected with "anthropopathy"—that is, the attribution to God of
human thought, feeling, and passion. In its present common usage
the former term has absorbed the distinctive meaning of the latter,
and is applied to the "projection" of any human character into any

non-human object. Anthropomorphism in this wider sense may crop up in all kinds of dealings between man and his world. The notions and practices of our primitive forefathers seem to have been saturated with it, and the habit of mind which was so strong in them still retains its hold upon us, sometimes showing itself openly, as in much poetic imagery, sometimes concealed in subtler forms. For instance, there is probably more than mere analogy in the "hands" of the clock and the "legs" of the table; there is a slight but unmistakable touch of anthropomorphic identification. And there is certainly anthropomorphism of the type more properly called anthropopathy in the "stubborn strength" we impute to the Norman keep and the "aspiration" we discern in the "soaring" pinnacle.

Students of folk-lore are not the only people interested in these two types of projection. Anthropomorphism has supplied psychologists of the Freudian school with many illustrations of their favourite doctrines; and anthropopathy, in the form he called *Einfühlung*, was made by Theodor Lipps the basis of a widely accepted theory of aesthetics. Again, critics of the history of science have not failed to note the part played by both types in the evolution of physical concepts. The man who spoke of "the prophetic soul of the wide world dreaming on things to come" was a poet; but contemporaries who were laying the foundations of modern science did not disdain to use the same ancient notion of an *anima mundi*. Hence Gilbert of Colchester could write in 1600, "Miserable were the condition of the stars, abject the lot of the earth, if that wonderful dignity of life be denied them, which is conceded to worms, ants, moths, plants and toadstools;"[1] and Kepler, in the introduction to his famous treatise, *De Motibus Stellae Martis* (1609), went so far as to use the admitted existence of planetary souls as an argument against the Ptolemaic hypothesis. How distracted, he says, must be the poor spirits who "ad tam multa respicere jubentur ut planetam duobus permixtis motibus invehant!"[2]

Anthropomorphic ideas of such crudity could be current among scientific men only so long as "Nature and Nature's laws lay hid in night." The epigram continues, "God said, Let Newton be, and all

1 *De Magnete* (Eng. ed., London: The Gilbert Club, 1900), p. 209.
2 *Opera*, ed. Frisch, Vol. III, p. 149.

was light." Yet hardly all. The vocabulary of mechanics—vis iner-
tiae, vis impressa, vis viva; centripetal and centrifugal force; work,
energy, least action—shows clearly that the new explorers of the
physical world continued to project into it, if not their souls, at
least their experiences of effort and resistance, of compulsion and
yielding. When Newton said "hypotheses non fingo" he may have
meant, among other things, that he did not use such terms seriously;[3] but there can be no question that they were used quite
seriously by his successors. For proof one need refer only to the
quasi-theological arguments of the Bernouillis, of Maupertuis, of
Mayer, and of our own Joule with respect to the nature and properties of energy. That is why the doctrines of Kirchhoff and Mach,
who declared that mechanics aims simply at describing natural
motions and has no concern with their causes, struck their contemporaries as paradoxical and subversive. Nor have the arguments
of those famous critics wholly prevailed against a tendency too
deeply rooted in human nature to be easily suppressed. The average
student of physics to-day is probably still at heart an anthropo-
morphist. He takes his science to be a hunt after causes and not
merely a search for what Lucretius, with fine inspiration, called
naturae species ratioque; and the causes he reads into nature almost
always convey into the transactions between material bodies features of the traffic between man's mind and his environment. Here
is one source of the prejudice against which the theory of relativity
had to make its way. For if a force is really a pull, or even if it is
only (as has been aptly said) the ghost of a pull, its intensity
cannot depend upon the motion of an observer any more than the
severity of my toothache depends upon the notice that other people
take of it. Yet, according to the new doctrine, forces have no intrinsic intensities, but are relegated to a status more insubstantial
even than the mathematical fictions to which Mach reduced them.

This illustration may seem to support the widespread notion that
Einstein's doctrine has destroyed the objectivity of physical science
and shown that the individual man is the measure of all things. I
must therefore point out that it is not so, and that writers who
claim that the physical doctrine of relativity leads inevitably to

[3] That is Mach's view. See *The Science of Mechanics* (2nd Eng. ed., London,
1902) , p. 183.

monadistic idealism have neglected to take due note of its most important feature. It is true that, according to the doctrine, the spatial and temporal elements in the panorama of events are not absolute, and change as one shifts the centre of regard. But it is overlooked, first, that the space-time frame does not depend upon the observer's mind, but upon the point of the material universe to which his body is attached; and, secondly, that the differences, from one point to another, are not in the least degree arbitrary but form an absolute system. Thus Einstein, instead of taking us back to or beyond Protagoras, has actually, as Professor Eddington says, carried notably farther the work of emancipation from anthropocentrism begun by Copernicus. The term "relativity" was, in truth, an unfortunate name to apply to a method of argument which starts out with the brave conviction that, however different the events of the world may look from different aspects, the order of nature is really one and absolute. To show that, in Minkowski's memorable words, space and time taken by themselves are but shadows was a spectacular feat; but the solid achievement of the new method is the way in which it uses the very relativity of time and space as a means of discovering the absolute features of physical laws. Consider, for instance, the principle of the conservation of momentum, which sums in a single expression Newton's three great laws of motion, and has, for that reason, long been regarded as one of the main foundations of nature's order. It involves the assumption that if M is a mass in motion with respect to two points A and B which are also in motion with respect to one another, then the velocity of M relative to B is simply its velocity relative to A compounded with the velocity of A relative to B.[4] But this assumption, regarded until recently, both by the man in the street and by the man of science, as unchallengeable, is now known to be untrue; for A and B, being in relative motion, have differing space and time systems. It follows that the classical expression of the principle of momentum must be erroneous, and the question arises how it is to be corrected. That question is answered by applying the simple canon that the true

[4] E.g. that if M, A, and B are moving the same way along a line, and M (as judged from A) is separating from A at the rate of 20 miles an hour, and A (as judged from B) is separating from B at the rate of 10 miles an hour, then M (as judged from B) is separating from B at the rate of 30 miles an hour.

form of the principle must be one which survives transference from one spatio-temporal system to another. And the application of the canon has led, in this instance, to the beautiful discovery that mass, so far from being constant, as Newton (who spoke of it as the quantity of matter in a body) supposed, actually varies with the body's velocity in relation to the centre of reference. In turn this rectification of the principle of momentum has explained certain behaviour of swift-moving particles shot out from radio-active matter. Einstein's correction of the Newtonian law of gravitation is only a particularly brilliant instance of the same method of procedure, applied still more boldly. Einstein's problem here was to find a set of equations which had no special reference to any particular space-time system but would, when applied to slow-moving bodies in the system, say of Greenwich Observatory, yield results sensibly in agreement with those deduced from Newton's law. Every one knows that the equations to which he was led by these canons not only explained a movement of the perihelion of Mercury which had long baffled the astronomers, but also suggested to the genius of the investigator that light-rays would be bent to a calculable extent in their passage near a massive body—a prediction confirmed both as to fact and as to amount by observations made during eclipses of the sun.

From such illustrations it should be clear that although observation can never get free from the restrictions of a particular space-time system, yet knowledge of the relations between one such system and others does enable us to reach universality conceptually—so far, that is, as the spatial and temporal forms of events are concerned. But relativity teaches nothing about the matter of the events as distinguished from their spatio-temporal forms: nothing, that is, about the lights and colours, the sounds, the odours, the hotnesses and coldnesses and so forth which we experience in space-time setting. For all that it has to tell us, these things may be of the very stuff of the universe. Relativity assures us that the shapes and sizes and durations of phenomena are not universal and yields principles of point-to-point correspondence between their varieties. But it gives no ground for thinking that the qualitative features of physical phenomena are projected into nature by the mind of man.

And yet the belief that colours, sounds, odours, hotnesses, and coldnesses *are* so projected is the orthodox and confident view of physical science. The great physicist, Max Planck, in the volume of addresses which suggested the subject as well as the title of this lecture,[5] maintains that the progress of theoretical physics has depended upon the degree to which investigators have succeeded in "a certain elimination of the anthropomorphous elements, particularly the specific sense-perceptions." Thus acoustics, which began as the science of sound-phenomena, has become the science of material vibrations, and as such has been completely absorbed into mechanics; the connexion of optics with vision has become irrelevant, and the science is now a branch of electro-dynamics; the science of heat has travelled so far away from the study of sensations of warmth and cold, that the term "temperature" now has reference not to an observer's feelings but to the kinetic energy of a body's molecular motion. The advantages that have followed from this liberation of physics from sense-perception are obvious. There is an elimination of the kind of contradiction that occurs when, for instance, a thing is pronounced by different observers to be at the same time warm and cold. There is the possibility of making records of phenomena which are both objective (and therefore of universal validity) and lasting—as when the temperature of the air at a certain place at a particular time is stated to be, say, 15° C. Lastly— and this is the point Planck stresses—the "elimination of the anthropomorphous elements" leads to the progressive unification of the physical sciences under wide-reaching general concepts. The instances I have just given exemplify the process, but Planck naturally draws his illustrations also from the field which his own genius has so brilliantly illuminated. Students of his *Wärmestrahlung* know well how, following Ludwig Boltzmann, he sought a mode of conceiving the principle of entropy which should be entirely free from the reference to human standards involved in the original way of regarding it; and how he was thus led to his epoch-making discovery of the quantum of energy. "Quantum theory" and "quantum mechanics" are at present most powerful and disturbing influences in theoretical physics, upsetting the peace of mind of the older investigators and tempting the younger ones into

5 Eng. trans. *A Survey of Physics* (London, 1925), pp. 7 ff.

the boldest intellectual adventures; but the quantum principle is
less an architectural law than a doctrine about the nature of the
material. For the supreme formula, embracing all others and so
occupying the highest position among physical laws, Planck refers
us to the principle of least action. This principle owes its dominance and its unifying power to its freedom from all "anthropomorphous elements," including the fact that it withstands Einstein's
test of universality—before which, as we have seen, other generalizations of the highest historic repute have broken down. Regarding
events, as it does, with an equal interest in the space they fill and
the time they occupy, it is the master-expression of the world's
eternal flux.[6]

It is of high importance to realize what price has been paid for
that unity of the physical sciences which can be reached, according
to the orthodox, only by the "elimination of the anthropomorphous." No one has, perhaps, made it clearer than Professor A. N.
Whitehead in a trenchant passage of his beautiful book, *Science
and the Modern World*.[7] We are required, he says to believe that

> Bodies are perceived as with qualities which in reality do not belong
> to them, qualities which in fact are purely the offspring of the mind.
> Thus nature gets credit which should in truth be reserved for ourselves:
> the rose for its scent: the nightingale for his song: and the sun for his
> radiance. The poets are entirely mistaken. They should address their
> lyrics to themselves, and should turn them into odes of self-congratula-
> tion on the excellency of the human mind. Nature is a dull affair, sound-
> less, scentless, colourless; merely the hurrying of material, endlessly,
> meaninglessly.

Here is, in brief, the philosophy which, as Whitehead observes,
has held its own as the guiding principle of scientific studies ever
since its birth in the mind of the seventeenth century, the "century
of genius." And to-day "it is not only reigning, but it is without a
rival." Nevertheless it is utterly incredible, and in truth is believed
by nobody. For the hardest-shelled man of science it is, so to speak,
only an official view of the world, maintained without question

---

[6] *A Survey of Physics*, pp. 127–128. Dr. L. Silberstein (*The Theory of Relativity*
[2nd ed., 1924], p. 457) holds that the importance of the principle of least action
has been exaggerated by some recent writers.

[7] (Cambridge, 1926) , p. 80.

during business hours for business purposes, but dropped silently, when business is over, for the common instinctive faith that music and laughter, the coloured beauty of living creatures and of sky, sea, mountain, and plain, even in some way the goodly savour of food, wine, and tobacco are realities—not phantasms dwelling only in the mind.

Whitehead has pointed out how deeply the modern mind is troubled by the discordance between the scientific materialism it professes and the attitude of the natural man which it instinctively shares, and there is, I suppose, no one who would not prefer the unsophisticated view of the world if it could be made intellectually respectable. To justify it one must, I think, prove three things: (i) that the assumption of the objective reality of sense-objects is not untenable; (ii) that the reality of the objects, such as ether and electrons, which physics offers as a substitute for such objects, is dubious; and (iii) that the results of physical investigation would still stand even though the usual interpretation of those results were rejected. I propose to speak briefly upon each of these matters.

There are two main reasons why reflective men have come to think that secondary qualities cannot belong to the reality of nature. One is that they appear to be irrelevant to what Professor Stout has called the executive order of the world. It is not the greenness of the grass that feeds the horse nor the sweetness of the honey that fills the comb. When a car collides with a pedestrian the victim's injuries are not put down to the sound of the horn or the colour of the bonnet. Secondary qualities seem, in short, to be in themselves insubstantial things and of importance only as indices of the properties that really matter. The other reason is that in attributing secondary qualities to things we constantly (it is said) contradict both other people and ourselves and often fall into error. The air cannot both be mild, as I feel it, and chilly, as you say it is; a penny cannot be both circular, as I see it, and elliptical, as it appears to you; a church cannot be both as small as it appears a mile away and as big as it seems when you are in the same street with it; a rose cannot really be red if the redness depends upon the presence of sunshine; and so on. Variations of this kind, which plainly follow upon changes in the conditions of perception, must, it is said, have their home in the perceiving mind; they cannot belong to the realm of objective things. And this is still more clearly true of the errors, as distinguished from the contradictions of sense: from regular and universal illusions such as the "straight staff bent in a pool," through the more variable illusions of the psychology books, down to the vagaries of colour-blind and misshapen eyes. To show that many of these errors are not really errors at all and that there is no real contradiction in the supposed contradictions would be too long an undertaking to attempt here; but it has been done elsewhere.[8] It must here suffice to point out why, if error and contradiction can be denied, they are so often confidently imputed.

The main reason is, I think, to be found in the predominance of the Aristotelian doctrine of οὐσία, which so enormously influenced western thought that belief in it, or some view derived from it, now seems to be instinctive. In every form of such belief, whether it is a precise philosophical or scientific doctrine or a vague popular idea, the essence is the distinction and contrast between the abiding "substance" of a thing and its changing phenomenal forms. And wherever this distinction is admitted there is bound to follow, sooner or later, χωρισμός or "bifurcation of Nature"[9] which leaves the "substance" in the "real" world, but relegates the phenomenal forms to the shadowy realm of mind. The classical scientific doctrine of the nature of things exhibits the χωρισμός in its sharpest form. Things are really pieces of "matter," unqualitied save in so far as they have shape and size, the properties of hardness and mass, and the mysterious powers of attracting or repelling one another; and their secondary qualities are merely psychical echoes in us of their collisions, direct or through air or ether, with the "matter" of our bodies. The only way to cure the symptoms of the disease is to extirpate their cause. If the classical concept of "matter" commits us to this intolerable "bifurcation of Nature," we must give it up. The alternative is to regard sense-objects not as appearances, or as effects of the activity, of the unknowable substance of a thing, but as genuine constituents of the thing; and, as I have already ventured

---

[8] I refer to the classical apologia for modern realism, Alexander, *Space, Time, and Deity*, Vol. I, to the writings of the American New Realists, to C. D. Broad, *Scientific Thought,* and to papers which I have, from 1904 onwards, contributed to the *Proceedings of the Aristotelian Society.*

[9] A. N. Whitehead, *Concept of Nature* (Cambridge, Eng., 1920) , esp. Chap. II.

to assert, that alternative is one which it is quite possible to maintain. What we see and hear and feel and taste are, in Professor Alexander's phrase, revelations of things; but what is revealed is not something other than the sense-objects, or sensa, themselves in their order and connexion. The order and connexion in the "revelation" of a thing are the abiding reality which the notion of substance symbolizes; they bind in an historic nexus all the sense-objects of which the thing is a source, not only for a single percipient but for all percipients. To borrow a term just now much used in psychology, the substance of a thing is the *Gestalt* of the sensa that enter into it. It follows that things may manifest degrees of substantiality varying with the definiteness and coherence of the *Gestalt*. At one end of the scale there is the compactness and solid endurance, say, of a coin; at the other end the stray smells and wandering noises of which Professor Whitehead somewhere speaks have their thin and fugitive existence. "It is not in virtue of a substance contained in them that things are; they are, when they are qualified to produce an appearance of there being a substance in them."[10]

To the unregenerate this concept of a material thing as a complex of sensa is bound to be difficult and unconvincing. A brilliant thinker, not quite persuaded, once said to me, "What I want to know is this: What cut King Charles's head off?" No one had rejected more decisively the old idea of matter, yet his question betrayed a lingering suspicion that Nature needs for her work firmer stuff than sensa are made on. Can the sharpness and temper of a steel blade be reduced to such vaporous elements? My reply is that in principle the reduction is quite possible; to tell the tale of King Charles's decapitation in terms of sensa only would be a prodigiously complicated and insufferably tedious business, but it could be done. And just because it would be so impracticably cumbrous we have learnt to cast our experience of things into the form of an abiding substance with changing appearances and manifestations of its nature. As I have observed elsewhere,[11] the process is akin to the one by which, according to Professor White-

---

[10] Lotze, *Metaphysics* (Eng. trans.) , Vol. I, p. 100.
[11] *Proceedings of the Aristotelian Society* (1924) , 8.

head, we unify in the idea of a point "without parts or magnitude" an endless series of related areas or volumes, all of which have both magnitude and parts. In both cases the "economy" brought about represents a quite extraordinary feat; but, as I pointed out on the same occasion, the greatness of the deed gives no reason for doubting its occurrence. If there is anything more wonderful than the complexity of our bodies, it is the unity with which the parts and functions conspire for the ends of life. And if the mind is (as in some way it surely is) an expression of the structure and properties of the body, it should not be surprising to find that it has been able to achieve and mechanize the processes involved in the conception of points and the perception of things.

From the beginning of my thoughts upon this subject it has seemed to me essential to insist (against Ernst Mach) upon the objectivity not only of the sensa included in a thing but also of the schema or *Gestalt* or nexus of the sensa.[12] Consider, for instance, a match-box which a diner holds and turns with his fingers while his fellow guests look at it, each from his own place at the table. There will be immediately present to the mind of the several observers distinct series of sensa. For the man who holds the match-box they will be largely tactual, for the rest they will be visual; but to all alike the sensa immediately present will (in Professor Whitehead's convenient phrase) "convey" other sensa not immediately present[13] —e.g. those corresponding to the unseen back and bottom of the box. Now the points to be noted are: (i) that the series of sensa directly presented to a particular observer is a coherent one, exhibiting an orderly sequence of shapes, visual or tactual; (ii) that the sensa "conveyed," no matter in what form they appear before the mind, adapt themselves in shape, size, and position to the directly apprehended sensa, much as the notes or the expectation of notes called up in one's mind by the opening bars of a familiar melody played on a piano adapt themselves in pitch, quality, and

---

[12] Cf. my book, *The Aim and Achievements of Scientific Method* (London, 1907), pp. 16–20.

[13] The complexity of the process and the difficulty in describing it accurately are brought out in the introspections recorded (*The Nature of Intelligence* [1923], pp. 196–200) by Professor Spearman, who gives an admirable analysis of it in conformity with his "noegenetic" principles.

intensity to the notes actually heard; and (iii) that these coherent series or bodies of actual and "conveyed" sensa, though differing from one another for observers sitting in different places, nevertheless enter into a larger coherence embracing both themselves and all other possible series of the same kind.[14] In its complete sense the substance of the match-box is the schema constituting this larger coherence. Considering this schema in relation to the schemas which govern the perceptions of the moving match-box by the several observers, we cannot fail to notice the analogy with the relation between individual orders of space and time and the absolute space-time order of nature. Mr. Bertrand Russell, referring to my views,[15] remarks that "two 'places' of different kinds are involved in every sense-datum [sensum], namely the place *at* which it appears and the place *from* which it appears." Correspondingly we must distinguish the "private space" of a particular percipient from the "perspective space" in which each private world counts as a spatial unit. The place *at* which a sensum is perceived is, upon this view, a place in a private space, and is not the same as a place in any other private space; nevertheless those places are, in practice, so easily correlated with one another that we have come to believe that when we view, each in his private space, an object, such as the small bright patch we call a star, we are actually looking at an identical object in a space common to us all. That space is, in fact, only a construction based upon our private spaces.

Doctrine of this kind seemed wild in the days before Professor Einstein had exhausted our capacity for astonishment. Now every one who understands the theory of relativity must at least suspect that something of the sort *must* be true. A doctrine of the physical object, worked out with full reference to that theory, has been adumbrated by Professor Whitehead in more than one of his recent books and is given in careful detail in *Science and the Modern World*. Its basis is the Bergsonian idea that the ultimate physical reality is a continuum of events, the "passage of Nature." But

14 We must recognize the possibility that this larger coherence may embrace elements—we must call them sensa for lack of a better term—which cannot be apprehended by human sense-organs.

15 *Mysticism and Logic* (London, 1918), pp. 152–155. The essay ("Sense-data and Physics") in which the reference occurs was written in 1914.

although we must speak of it in that way, the physical absolute is not an historical procession of events through space; it assumes that character only with reference to a particular event of the continuum taken as a standpoint; and the abstract spatio-temporal frame in which the procession is set varies, in accordance with the theory of relativity, from one such standpoint to another. When the standpoint chosen is occupied by a "percipient event" the world is actually perceived as a particular temporal flux taking place in a particular space; but even if we choose a standpoint, A, not thus occupied—say, an event occupied by the being of a stone—everything is the same as before, barring the perceiving. The world's flux is no longer *ap*prehended at the standpoint, A, but it is still "prehended" there. This notion of prehension is fundamental. It means that the parts of a volume or of a stretch of time have no independent existence but "form an ordered aggregate, in the sense that each part is something from the standpoint of every other part, and also from the same standpoint every other part is something in relation to it."[16] If A and B are, for instance, two volumes, the aspect of B from A is of the essence of A; it may be described as the mode in which B enters into the composition of A. Prehension is the name for the way in which the aspects of all other volumes or times from the standpoint A enter into unity in A. As we have already seen, when A is the percipient activity of a human being, the prehensive unity becomes apprehension. It appears, then, that A's space and time may be said to be in A and yet at the same time to be located in the events B, C, D, &c., since they are aspects of those events that come into prehensive unity in A. The shape of a volume is more abstract than its aspects; it is "the formula from which the totality of its aspects can be derived." The simplicity of time, we may add, excludes anything analogous to shape, or there would be an analogous statement to make about it.

What has been said about space and time, which are the most abstract characters of events, applies in principle to their more concrete characters. For instance, a patch of green, seen at B from A, "is not simply at A where it is being perceived, nor is it simply at B where it is perceived as located; but it is present at A with the

---

[16] *Science and the Modern World* [Cambridge, England] (1926) , p. 95.

mode of location in B."[17] It seems a fair inference from this (though I am not sure whether Whitehead would accept it) that the green exists with reference to the standpoint A exactly as the relevant space-time system exists.[18] Doubtless an eye is needed at A, with a brain behind it, in order that the green may be *seen;* but it *exists* at A "with the mode of location in B" whether there is an eye there or not. The inference, if legitimate, would to me be a welcome one; for I have always thought it desirable, if not actually necessary, that the kind of realism I am defending should include a belief in the existence of sensa whether they are perceived or not.

Objects[19] are, for Whitehead, characters of events, the events being the "situations" of the objects. Leaning over a bridge one sees a constant reflection of one's form in the stream, though the water which reflects the image is incessantly changing, Analogously a flux of events may retain a particular character for an indefinite period. It is important to distinguish two types of objects which may, in different ways, occupy an event. The one type is the sense-object or sensum, such as the patch of green at B. This, as we have seen, is not simply located at B; for its location at B is a factor in the prehension at A, and aspects of other events which enter into the prehension at A may be necessary to it: for instance, sunlight. The other type is the physical object, here the blade of grass, of which the sensum is (in my terminology) a constituent. That must be conceived as independent of any particular standpoint A; and so far as I can understand him, Whitehead's doctrine about it is substantially the same as mine: namely, the physical object is a schema that controls the emergence of sensa into particular "prehensions."

So far the argument has been that what Whitehead calls a "provisional realism" is tenable; that it pictures the physical world as

17 *Op. cit.,* p. 103.

18 Cf. the following passage: "Nature is a structure of evolving processes. The reality is the process. It is nonsense to ask if the colour red is real. The colour red is ingredient in the process of realization. The realities of nature are the prehensions in nature, that is to say, the events in nature." *Op. cit.,* p. 106. I am not sure whether this means only that the colour red is real in an actual process of perception from A, or whether it means that it may be real even though A is not occupied by a "percipient event." Cf. *The Principle of Relativity,* p. 33.

19 Miss L. S. Stebbing has given, in her paper in *Proc. of the Aris. Soc.* (1925–6), the most acute analysis of Professor Whitehead's theory of objects with which I am acquainted.

something infinitely more complex than common sense thinks it to
be, yet preserves against the assaults of scientific theory those features which are essential to the common-sense view. We have next
to deal with the "scientific objects" which physics offers us as the
reality behind the veil of sensible appearances, the invisible agents
of the flux of nature; and the purpose of my argument here is to
cast doubt upon their existence. A simple instance of a scientific
object is caloric, the fluid whose transference from one body to
another was supposed to cause the temperature of the former to fall
and of the latter to rise until a state of equilibrium was attained.
The eighteenth century thought of caloric simply as an invisible,
intangible form of matter, subtler than the other chemical elements,
yet belonging to the same order of being: in Thomas Thomson's
classification, it was an "unconfinable simple substance"—i.e. one
that, unlike gases, it was not possible to retain in a bottle.[20] Caloric
and the "electric fluid" which appeared in scientific writings in the
same epoch were scientific, as distinguished from natural or physical
objects, inasmuch as they were inferred not observed entities,
hypotheses read into the context of physical phenomena, not things
found there. To put the point crudely, no one ever claimed to have
observed either of these fluids, only the results of their supposed
existence and movements. But they were not scientific objects in the
sense that ether was for the nineteenth century and electrons are for
the twentieth. When Oliver Heaviside declared that ether and
energy were the only physical realities and that all else was moonshine, he did not think of ether (as Thomson thought of caloric) as
a substance among substances; he thought of it as the primal and
ultimate substance from which all specific forms of materiality are
derived. Similarly, electrons and protons, whether conceived as
ultimate particles of electricity or as ultimate particles of matter
charged with electricity (whatever the difference may mean) are
not regarded by the physicist as bodies in a world containing other
bodies. They are ultimately the only material bodies that exist, all
other bodies, as we seem to see, hear, smell, taste, feel them, being
only the way in which our perceptive faculties react to gigantic
clusters of the primary particles, in enormously complicated modes

20 Thomas Thomson, *A System in Chemistry in Five Volumes* (4th ed., London,
1810) , Vol. I, p. 424.

of movement. It follows that though we may ascribe size, shape, and mass to electrons, they have no secondary qualities; they, whose behaviour is the cause of our sensations of light, colour, fragrance, and temperature, cannot themselves be luminous or coloured or odorous or hot or cold.

Now there seem to me to be two strong reasons for disbelieving in the existence of such scientific objects, one metaphysical, the other historical. The metaphysical argument was indicated long ago by Bishop Berkeley. Briefly it is that experience discloses sizes and shapes as features of only one kind of material, namely, sensa, and gives no warrant whatever for ascribing them to anything else. As we have just seen, a physical object, such as a coin, has not really a single shape or size. The circular shape we ascribe to it is but the shape of certain of its constituent sensa, and is selected from among the variety of forms presented by the whole series because it holds among them a typical or representative position; geometrically, it is the central term from which the other (elliptical) forms derive symmetrically, and it is the form seen when the coin is held in the best position for observation. Again, the size we ascribe to a coin when, for instance, we say that the diameter of a half-crown measures an inch and a quarter, is not an absolute size; the statement is merely a condensed way of saying that if the coin is laid upon an inch-scale there will be coincidence between its edges and certain graduations of the scale. Like the shapes, the sizes that belong absolutely to the coin, being the bignesses of its constituent sensa, are indefinitely numerous. In sum, in thinking of a coin as possessing a single shape and a single size we perform upon the vast assemblages of sensa that constitute it an act similar to the act in which we think of a certain unique "enclosure-series" of areas or volumes as a point possessing no parts or magnitude. To one who is convinced of the truth of this account of the constitution of a physical object and of the process of perceiving it, the notion of an unqualitied piece of matter, such as the electron is held to be, becomes quite incredible. For if the only shapes, sizes, and positions we know are those of sensa, how can an electron, into whose constitution, by hypothesis, no sensa enter, have position or size or shape?

This is the metaphysical argument. It appears to me to be conclusive, but I grant that it derives its force from a general theory which cannot compel universal assent. The second argument does not suffer from this defect; for it is based upon facts beyond dispute. It aims at discrediting all scientific objects by showing that in the history of science they have been constantly found out and discarded.

Caloric, to which I have already referred, offers a simple illustration of the thesis. Joseph Black conceived it as a substance capable of quantitative estimation, whose transference from body to body accounted for changes of temperature and such phenomena as the transformation of ice into water. This conception guided him to discoveries of high importance, and so late as 1824 was central in those reflections of Sadi Carnot upon the motive power of heat in which began the science of thermodynamics. Yet investigations prompted by Black's notion of caloric had already led to the knowledge of truths incompatible with it. Count Rumford had shown that heat can be produced in indefinite amount by friction, as in the boring of cannon, and Davy had clinched his argument by proving that two pieces of ice may be melted simply by rubbing them together. In the face of such facts the conception of caloric was at length abandoned, and replaced by the idea that heat is, as Tyndall said in his famous lectures, a mode of motion. But although no one now believes in caloric, it is instructive to note that the ideas of the old theory still live in the terms "specific heat," "thermal capacity," "latent heat," and are the high road along which every beginner enters into this essential branch of physics. In short, the notion that thermal phenomena are due to an "unconfinable simple substance" proved useful for two reasons: first because it enabled the inquirer to bring the observed facts into an orderly connexion by means of a concrete and very familiar image, and secondly because the image suggested further analogies between the thermal behaviour of bodies and the behaviour of a fluid, and so led to further discoveries. The former, the psychological, value of the notion still remains and every teacher and student profits by it. The latter, the heuristic, value came to an end when facts which the notion itself had brought to light proved fatal to it.

Much the same can be said about electricity, which the natural philosophers of the eighteenth century also thought of as a fluid. Here again an analogy which guided the earlier investigators still governs the technical vocabulary of a science and shapes all elementary and popular knowledge about it. The most erudite physicists continue to speak about electric "currents" and the man in the generating station, lending to the idea the superior vividness of slang, speaks of the commodity his dynamo supplies as "juice." Yet the notion of a fluid, or of a pair of fluids, flowing round the electric circuit has long ceased to be adequate to the known facts. In 1889 Sir Oliver Lodge,[21] expounding the consequences of Maxwell's ideas, explained that the real function of the wire is to guide the etherial energy, which might well be held to "flow" everywhere *except* in the circuit. Since then electronic theory has rehabilitated the current in the wire; but it is now conceived as a flow not of a fluid but of minute constituents of the metallic atoms. Thus it will be seen that the continuity in the use of the term "electricity" during the last 150 years masks profound changes in the concept of the scientific object which it is supposed to name; and that, as in the parallel case of heat, the earlier concepts have been rendered untenable by the discoveries to which they themselves have led.

The case of ether is still more illuminating, for the nineteenth century pinned to it a faith which the twentieth has transferred to the electron. An understanding of ether, it was thought, was the key to all the mysteries of the material universe; ether and energy were the only realities, all else was but "moonshine." The reality of ether seemed to be very real when confident calculations were made of its elasticity and other properties; and when one considers the magnificent services the idea rendered to science in the hands of the great physicists of the nineteenth century from Fresnel and Maxwell to Larmor and Lorentz, the conviction that it was the fundamental thing in nature is very intelligible. Yet here again history repeated itself. Exploration of the ether theory in the study and the laboratory led to results which made it impossible to hold it in anything like its original simplicity. The famous experiment of Michelson and Morley was not the only cause of its downfall. The successors of Maxwell, developing their great inheritance, found it necessary to strip ether of all its mechanical properties except immobility; the special theory of relativity, based largely upon the negative results

21 *Modern Views of Electricity,* p. 238.

of the Michelson and Morley experiment, merely completed the deprivation.[22] Thus ether lost its character of *prima materia* and ceased even to be able, as a quasi-material all-pervading medium, to render the phenomena of radiation intelligible. But the theory of relativity, which hastened the dematerialization of ether, has acted in the opposite way upon the concept of space. Space is no longer to be regarded as indifferent to the events that work themselves out in it; it takes a hand in them. Thus the two concepts, of ether and of space, have approached one another, and may now be regarded as identical.

Lastly we come to the electron, which is the reigning monarch in physical theory. Is it to be its fate also to be devoured by its children, or is its kingdom secure for ever? When we consider the men who have given their allegiance to it and the magnitude of the conquests they have achieved in its name, it seems impertinent to question the permanence of its rule—until one remembers how great were the votaries of ether, and what triumphs they won under its banner. It is true that experiment seems to have brought us so near to verification of the electron that only as obstinate doctrinaire could resist the evidence for its existence, and there seems here to be a vital difference between this case and those of caloric and of ether. Nevertheless there are not only the metaphysical arguments, whatever they may be worth, but there are also scientific considerations which seem to justify scepticism even in the face of C. T. R. Wilson's and R. A. Millikan's miraculous experiments and measurements.

The concept of an electron as an atom of electricity was born far back in the last century—the name was introduced by Johnstone Stoney in 1891—but the exciting phase of its history began when Sir E. Rutherford formulated the planetary scheme of the atom which has gained universal acceptance, and his pupil, Professor Niels Bohr, developed this into a mathematical theory which, when applied to the simple case of the hydrogen atom, linked together with astonishing success the hypothetical radii of the electronic orbits, Planck's quantum-constant and the empirically known law governing the distribution of lines in the spectrum of hydrogen.

[22] Einstein, *Sidelights on Relativity* (Eng. trans., 1922), p. 11.

But, for our purpose, the important thing to note is that Bohr won his triumph only at the cost of a very serious break with classical electrodynamics. According to the orthodox theory a negative electron should be emitting energy all the time it is revolving about the central positive mass or proton; yet if it did so, the radius of its orbit would rapidly contract, and the planet would shortly fall into its sun. Such a catastrophe, which would be accomplished normally within a minute fraction of a second, must be expressed in those properties which have led physicists to assign a definite initial radius to the electron's orbit and to associate it with a definite feature in the hydrogen spectrum. But nothing of the sort has been observed. Professor Bohr took, accordingly, the bold step of declaring, flat in the face of the classical theory, that nothing of the sort occurs. His hypothesis is that the electron radiates no energy so long as it revolves in a particular orbit, and that no gradual change in the radius of the orbit is possible. There are, however, a series of distinct and separate orbits which the electron may occupy, and from time to time it disappears from one of these and reappears in another. If the second orbit is smaller than the first, this extraordinary event is accompanied by the release of a definite parcel or quantum of energy—a "quantum" being Planck's ultimate unit or atom of energy; and, since the energy is emitted in the form of radiation, Planck's formula enables the frequency of this radiation to be calculated. What has given Bohr's hypothesis its present dominant position is that the frequencies to which it points are the actual frequencies of the radiations that constitute the hydrogen spectrum.

There can, then, be no question that Bohr's mathematical theory corresponds to important facts about the minute structure of the material world, but it seems equally clear that the model of image which he uses to put his mathematics into an intuitable form cannot be taken seriously.[23] According to the original conception, an electron was a minute piece of matter, even though the matter were "electricity." That means that it was supposed to have a

[23] For an example of attempts to modify the model in such a way as to avoid the breach with classical theory, see D. Wrinch, "Scientific Methodology with Special Reference to Electron Theory," *Proc. of the Aris. Soc.* (1926–7) , 52 ff. The device Dr. Wrinch considers is the "spinning electron" of L. V. King.

definite time; it also means that it was subject to the laws of the Newtonian dynamics and, since it was electrical, to Maxwell's electrodynamics which are based upon Newton's system and are of a piece with it. In other words, the statement that the atom was like a minute solar system was meant to be taken seriously, with the qualification that the forces involved were electrical, not gravitational. But the Bohr atom, though it masquerades as such a system, refuses to behave like one. It owns no firm allegiance to the fundamental principles that govern the behaviour of matter wherever matter can actually be observed, but picks and chooses those it will follow. Thus it is obedient as regards the orbits of its electrons, but flatly contumacious as regards the radiation they ought to emit. When to these more recondite considerations one adds the simple fact that the electron is supposed to "switch" from orbit to orbit without taking any actual journey from one to the other, it is plain that whatever we are dealing with in electrons and protons we are certainly far away from the "matter" with which experience has made us familiar. Even a layman may, without much presumption, go farther and guess that since the electron, which started out, like ether before it, with nothing but straightforward mechanical properties, now finds itself obliged, again like ether, to assume other properties incompatible with these, its ultimate disappearance from physical theory is foreshadowed. Its existence is, in fact, becoming too complicated to be supported.

Whitehead, speaking upon this question with a knowledge to which I cannot make the smallest claim, remarks that "the physical theory of the atom has got into a state which is strongly suggestive of the epicycles of astronomy before Copernicus."[24] In what direc-

---

[24] *Science and the Modern World*, p. 190. Cf. the following passage which appeared in print after the lecture was given: "The truly mechanical features of the orbit scheme (speaking from the standpoint of classical mechanics) have retreated farther and farther into the background, and the willingness of the theoretical physicists to sacrifice dynamical sanity for the temporary description of an empirical rule has been occasionally bewildering. The quantum theory has become, in its higher branches, a collection of numerical receipts, to which a superficial resemblance to a coherent mathematical theory has been given to hide their *ad hoc* character. The difficulty of understanding them is not mathematical but fundamental. Some of the rules recall irresistibly the teaching of the alchemists, or the witches' kitchen in *Faust*." E. N. da C. Andrade, *The Structure of the Atom* (3rd ed., 1927), p. 708.

ton, then, is a Copernican simplification to be looked for? This is a problem, of immense complexity and difficulty, which is employing and is likely long to employ the best mathematical physicists in the world. Professor Whitehead has himself referred[25] to one possible and promising line of advance which has been followed by the physicists de Broglie and Schrödinger.[26] It avoids the paradox that an electron may be now here and then there without traversing the region between the two places by supposing that it consists not in "matter" but in groups of waves. For there is nothing outrageous in the idea that a group of waves may sink into the ocean, its energy being represented by the simultaneous emergence of another group elsewhere. Professor Max Born has described in a recent series of lectures[27] an alternative method of dealing with the "quantum-mechanics" of the atom and spectral phenomena which has been developed by him in collaboration with Dr. Heisenberg and Dr. Jordan and independently by Mr. Dirac at Cambridge. The fundamental principle of the method is not new, though the mathematical calculus invented for its application is highly novel, ingenious, and (I must confess) difficult. It is similar to the principle worked out years ago, on the basis of Lagrange's dynamics, by Sir J. J. Thomson.[28] In brief it makes no pretence to explain physical phenomena in terms of hidden mechanisms, such as those postulated in the Bohr theory, but sets out merely to analyse them in terms of entities that can be actually observed, such as energy-levels, the associated light-frequencies, and the average volume which an atom occupies as its territory. It relinquishes the idea of expressing

---

25 *Op. cit.*, pp. 52–6.

26 A clear account of their work is given in Biggs, *Wave Mechanics* (1927). I have to thank Lord Haldane for calling my attention to this useful little book. For the knowledge I possessed when the lecture was given I was largely indebted to communications from Mr. Basil Fletcher, Research Fellow of Sidney Sussex College.

27 *Probleme der Atomdynamik* (1926). An English version is also published.

28 *Applications of Dynamics to Physics and Chemistry* (1888). See T. P. Nunn, "On Causal Explanation," *Proc. of the Aris. Soc.* (1906–7). It is also similar, as Professor Andrade points out, to the procedure followed by Einstein in the development of the theory of relativity. (See *op. cit.*, "Concluding Remarks," where a brief but illuminating description of the new mechanics is given.) The *Mathematical Gazette* (December, 1926), contains a useful account of Born's book in the form of a review by Professor Piaggio.

the results obtained in the form of statements about the orbit of an electron and its position at a given time; for not only does it seem impossible in principle even to measure atomic dimensions, it is doubtful whether such geometrical propositions have, when applied to the ultra-microscopic world, their usual meaning.[29] Nevertheless, just as Einstein's laws of motion shade into Newton's when the velocities of the bodies under consideration are relatively small, so the quantum mechanics becomes identical with the classical doctrine when applied to volumes sufficiently big.[30]

"Wave mechanics" and "quantum-mechanics" are highly technical as well as novel branches of physical theory with which few professional physicists claim familiarity and to which a layman may at present refer only in terms of distant respect. So far, however, as I understand their purport, they both seek to assimilate to the classical tradition the facts that, in Bohr's theory, were left in a painful state of conflict with it; and both seem to have succeeded in doing so. From the logical point of view that is in itself a great achievement. It now remains for the new theories to prove that they not only are logically more acceptable than the older one but also embrace more facts and have a greater heuristic power. As regards the former of these points, I understand that they have both been far more successful than the older theory in accounting for the intensities of spectral lines; as regards the latter their virtue has still to be explored. The interest, however, with which they are now being studied and the expectations that are formed of their future development may be claimed as justifying the doubts, based mainly upon metaphysical grounds, which some of us have for many years felt about the "reality" of the electron *et hoc genus omne* of scientific objects. In brief, the approaching supersession of the electron is another and powerful piece of evidence against the view that the

29 Cf. Eddington, *The Mathematical Theory of Relativity* (1923), p. 225: "It is a fallacy to think that the conception of location in space-time based on the observation of large-scale phenomena can be applied unmodified to the happenings which involve only a small number of quanta."

30 The same thing is true of de Broglie and Schrödinger's wave-mechanics. The relation between wave-mechanics and the classical mechanics is analogous to the difference between wave-optics and ray-optics. Just as analysis in terms of ray-optics breaks down when light-phenomena in small regions are investigated, and must be replaced by the analytic methods of wave-optics, so wave-mechanics replaces classical mechanics in the analysis of atomic motions.

history of the physical world is the history of swarms of ultimate particles of "matter" in perpetually changing configuration.

To say this is not to commit the absurdity of denying the immensely important part the classical electronic theory has played in the discovery and investigation of new facts. On the contrary that theory must be credited with one discovery of supreme interest and significance: namely, that microphysical phenomena follow principles which cannot be inferred from the principles derived from the study of the macrophysical. This result was, at the outset, quite unexpected; for electronic theory started out to account for observable phenomena in terms of the action of ultimate particles of electricity or electrified matter whose properties were those of the electrified bodies of laboratory experiments. In other words, the idea of the electron, like the ideas of caloric, electricity, the atom of Dalton, and the luminiferous ether, was derived directly from everyday experience of physical objects. The electron is a charged body reduced conceptually to a minute size and, like the other scientific objects I have named, stripped conceptually of any irrelevant or inconvenient properties.[31] It was, accordingly, assumed to follow in essential matters the behaviour of laboratory bodies, and the discovery that it does not do so was a startling surprise. That discovery is, as I have urged, a proof that in picturing the minute behaviour of "matter" physicists had followed a wrong analogy, that is, had fastened upon the wrong kind of model; and recalling what has happened to other scientific objects that once received equal confidence, I claim it, further, as evidence that *no* model based upon the substance-and-attribute concept of matter can ever have more than temporary success. This prediction is based upon the belief that the substance-and-attribute concept gives an untrue account even of ordinary physical objects, since the "substance" of such objects is but the form of connexion or coherence of the sensa which are their actual constituents. It follows from this view, as I have already tried to show, that a substance without sensible qualities, that is, a form of connexion which connects nothing, is an absurdity.

The reality of the physical objects of common sense consists (I

31 Cf. Nunn, "Sense Data and Physical Objects," *Proc. of the Aris. Soc.,* (1915–16) , 175 ff., and previous papers there cited.

repeat) in the reality of their constituent sensa and of the form of connexion of these. There is also a reality corresponding to the term "electron," but, on my view, it consists also of nothing but sensa and their form of connexion. Professor Whitehead has said that "when Sir Ernest Rutherford knocks a molecule to pieces, he does not see a molecule or an electron. What he observes is a flash of light,"[32] and the remark will help to make my meaning clear. The flash of light, spectral rays, and a vast host of other observable things, with perhaps a vaster host of others unobservable by man's senses, are the constituents of the electron, and the substance of the electron is their characteristic mode of connexion. In thinking of the electron as a localized unqualitied body the physicists have repeated the error in the common view about physical objects,[33] but in conceiving it as atomic they are probably completely right. Time was when the great globe itself, yea all that it inherits, had as yet no being, and time may come when it shall dissolve. The cloud-capped towers, the solemn temples, the gorgeous palaces are group-ings and coherences of sensa which had a beginning and may have an end. But the grouping and coherence of sensa that constitute a particular electron, if the electron is truly atomic or ultimate, are eternal.[34] And, as Professor Max Born has observed,[35] the fact that through the light thrown upon them by quantum theory, electronic processes are now seen always to be correlated with whole numbers, gives good reason to believe that such processes really are ultimate. Thus modern science appears finally to have justified, in principle, the instinctive belief of Democritus. But in finding that atomic coherences differ essentially from those which appear in ordinary physical objects it has qualified the ancient creed of materialism in a most important way. It is likely that this discovery, together with Einstein's discovery of the relativity of space and time, will have an influence upon the general outlook of civilized mankind at least as profound as the influence we trace to Copernicus.

The modern physics and chemistry of the atom are based upon

---

[32] *The Principle of Relativity* (1922) , p. 61.

[33] This statement does not deny the special significance of the "singular point" in the world-wide structure of the electron where the "particle" is supposed to exist.

[34] Cf. Whitehead, *The Concept of Nature*, p. 171.

[35] *Probleme der Atomdynamik,* p. 2.

the classical concept of the electron. Even if electrons should come to be believed in, like caloric, by no men of science or, like the ether, by very few, it is therefore probable that, like both caloric and the ether, they will continue to govern the vocabulary of physics and chemistry and to determine the form taken by expositions of those sciences. But if the electron becomes *démodé*, what will replace it? Will workers at the growing-point of physics follow henceforward the purely descriptive methods of Heisenberg or, as in the past, simply exchange the old physical model for a new one? The need of a concrete analogy to guide research in a new field is so strongly felt by most minds,[36] even of the highest order, that it is safe to predict for the second course at least a large following. As we have seen, de Broglie and Schrödinger have already come forward with a model alternative to the planetary model of Rutherford and Bohr, and it is most interesting and instructive to note that in inventing it they have fallen back upon the other great classical notion of mathematical physics, namely, wave-motion. In their theory the electron as a particle is replaced by a wave-group produced by the mutual reinforcement of a set of waves. There is, further, an attempt to conceive the radiation from the electron as consisting in "beats" produced by the interference of such sets; but I gather that there is a serious difficulty in bringing the second branch of the theory into proper relation with the first. But whether this difficulty is overcome or not, the emergence of a theory which reduces matter to waves inevitably brings up the question, waves of *what?* Is the ether to be rehabilitated and made once more, with energy, the foundation of all things?

Greatly daring, I venture to believe that the only ether that can henceforward hold its own is what Professor Whitehead calls an "ether of events." For some years before I learnt this phrase from him I maintained that the essential thing implied by the term ether is the existence of far-spreading sets of events whose date, magnitude, and other general characteristics depend in a regular way upon their distance from the particular event which is regarded as their source. For instance, if a momentary spark is produced at a

---

[36] One remembers that Lord Kelvin could not accept Clerk Maxwell's theory of the electro-magnetic displacement because he could not devise a mechanical model for it.

given point in space, then any suitable piece of apparatus, such as an eye or a photographic plate, suitably oriented, will become the seat of an event of calculable intensity happening a calculable time after the spark. If, as is generally the case, the original event is periodic in character, the derived events will display corresponding periodicities and, in their sequence, will exhibit the features which we call wave-motion. Yet there need be no actual motion of anything and no medium to convey the "undulations." Professor Whitehead, if I understand him aright, adds to this strictly empirical notion the assumption that something is always happening everywhere, that is, that space-time is a continuum of events. Thus his usage of the term ether retains the old notion that the ether is all-pervading, while mine, though compatible with that notion, does not imply it. In other words, I prefer to suppose provisionally that where no events can be observed no event is happening.

These remarks lead the way to some final considerations. If, in dealing with linked events such as those just referred to, we exclude the notion of a connecting medium, we may take our stand upon one of two distinct positions. We may assume that there really is between all the events of the world the "uniformity of relatedness" which Kant explained as due to the uniform intuitive activity of the mind. This assumption enables us to maintain the "old-fashioned belief in the fundamental character of simultaneity," while recognizing, in accordance with the special theory of relativity, that nature submits to alternative systems of temporal stratification. It also allows us to believe that we can know these temporal "slabs" of nature, partly through "cognizance by adjective" (i.e. by direct observation of the characters of events), partly through "cognizance by relatedness" beyond the bounds of direct observation. If we start from this position we may further suppose that upon the uniform relatedness of events there are superimposed contingencies which take the form of the appearance in events of particular adjectives or characters. These appearances are contingent, because observation of them does not carry with it any certain knowledge of other adjectives. Nevertheless we are able empirically to ascertain connexions, which we call the laws of nature, which seem to regulate the appearance of specific adjectives of events throughout the whole extent and course of nature; and our power to discriminate these connexions depends upon the fact that they are atomic, i.e. constitute systems of adjectives which are independent of other systems. Here, expressed very baldly, is the view taken by Professor Whitehead and defended by him as a criticism of Professor Einstein.[37]

The other position is the one developed by Einstein in his general theory of relativity. It may be said to assume that space-time is not merely a system of relatedness between events but part (if not actually the whole) of their very stuff. It seems therefore to be essentially identical with the position assumed by Professor Alexander in *Space, Time, and Deity*. As we all know, Einstein has succeeded in reducing the contingencies known as gravitational effects to local differences in the character of space-time. It is also widely known that a brilliant disciple, Professor Hermann Weyl, going farther along the same path, has sought to bring about a similar reduction of electromagnetic phenomena. The following account, based upon Professor Eddington's modification of Weyl's theory, may suffice to give a general idea of the argument.[38] Let a rod be moved from one place to another in a region of space. Then if the region is a gravitational field the length of the rod, according to Einstein's theory, will change, but its length in any given place will be the same, no matter by what route it reaches that place. Now let us introduce the further supposition that the change in the length of the rod depends upon the route by which it has been taken from the first position to the second. Then the relevant geometrical differential equations take a form which has the striking character that it is identical with the form of the fundamental equations of the electromagnetic field. Thus we have only to assume that the identity is not merely formal but real, and electromagnetism, like gravitation, ceases to be an ultimate and inexplicable feature of the physical world, but appears, also like gravitation, as an expression of local variations in the character of space-time.

I am totally unqualified to discuss the validity of Weyl's astonishing deduction[39] or to adjudicate between Whitehead and Einstein.

---

[37] See Whitehead, *The Principle of Relativity* (1922), esp. Chap. IV, from which my quotations are taken.

[38] I follow the much simplified explanation given in Jeans, *Mathematical Theory of Electricity and Magnetism* (5th ed., 1925), pp. 623 ff.

[39] Einstein, I understand, rejects it.

Whitehead's view of space-time seems to be an integral part of his metaphysics of nature and to be bound up specially closely with his doctrine of prehension. For that reason, as well as for others, I should like to think it true. On the other hand, I am not sure that when Einstein assumes that space-time has everywhere the character expressed by the contracted Riemann-Christoffel tensor he has not granted the "uniformity of relatedness" which Whitehead demands. It is true that he seeks to reduce to modifications of space-time the contingencies known as gravitational effects, but these contingencies seem to be, like Whitehead's, superimposed upon a thoroughgoing uniformity. The point at issue seems accordingly to be the one to which I have already referred, namely, whether space-time is, as Whitehead holds, merely an abstraction from events, or, as Alexander maintains, "the stuff of which all finite things are made." But however this issue is decided, the imagination must be dull that does not see in the mathematical work of Einstein and Weyl one of the most amazing and exciting adventures of the human intellect. And my own admiration of their achievements is made more enjoyable by the powerful support they lend to the belief that there is in the physical world nothing but sensa and their modes of connexion.

5

Causality in Contemporary Physics

by MORITZ SCHLICK

EDITORIAL NOTE: *The intellectual affiliations between philosophical positivism and the orthodox interpretations of quantum mechanics began to show themselves in the writings of Werner Heisenberg, Max Born and Niels Bohr from 1926 onward; and their alliance is symbolized in the present essay, which was originally published in the authoritative German scientific periodical,* Die Naturwissenschaften, *in 1931. As the professional heir of Ernst Mach, Moritz Schlick had taken over the leadership of the young radical group of scientifically oriented philosophers who came to be known as the* Wiener Kreis *(Vienna Circle) —a group as close and polemical in its own way as the Freudian circle of psychoanalysts and the other contemporary cultural groups that sprang up in the years just before and after World War I.*

The Vienna Circle philosophers moved away from Mach in one significant respect: they found the ultimate basis for their theory of knowledge less in sense data *than in* physical observables, *such as pointer-readings and marks on photographic plates—cf. Schlick's essay, sec. 7, p. 98. In this respect their philosophical ideas were "physicalist" rather than "sensationalist," as befitted their program for a "unified science" based on the methods of a logically self-aware physics. Yet in most other respects they followed Mach in his commitment to positivist principles. Thus we find Schlick, in this very essay, explicating the notion of causality in terms that appeal to the "verification principle" (sec. 6), making the possibility of predicting one event on the basis of another a "sufficient" criterion of their causal connectedness (sec. 7), distinguishing sharply be-*

*tween "tautologies" and genuinely empirical "assertions" (sec. 9),
and citing Hume's analysis of causality as authoritative throughout
(especially sec. 11).*

*It was on the analytical groundwork laid by such essays as this
that John von Neumann in due course offered his attempted demonstration that any future system of theoretical physics must respect
the limits, on empirical observability and theoretical analysis alike,
expressed in Heisenberg's fundamental equation. Yet, if we read
between the lines, we can already see in Schlick's own exposition
the point at which all such demonstrations would in due course be
open to attack. For, as Schlick puts it, "The principle of indeterminacy is an integral part of the structure of the quantum theory,
and we must trust its correctness so long as new experiments and
new observations do not force us to revise the quantum theory"
(sec. 8 at end). Any proof of the unique intellectual authority of
quantum mechanics based on the assumed universality, at every
level of analysis, of quantum-mechanical principles, will therefore
be circular. Still, Schlick did well to show how the principle of
causality functions, within physics, as the expression of a methodological precept and/or ideal; and to emphasize that a full-scale commitment to the new quantum mechanics required the physicist to
restrict his intellectual ambitions and to limit the range of phenomena which he could, in principle, regard as explicable or intelligible.*

1. INTRODUCTORY REMARKS

THE NUMBER OF conceivable, logically possible, physical worlds is
infinite; the human imagination, however, is surprisingly poor in
conceiving and working out new possibilities. The power of imagination is so limited by the intuitive conditions of gross perceptual
experience that it can hardly by itself progress a step beyond them.
It is only by aid of the strict discipline of more refined scientific
experience that our thought can transcend its habitual channels.
The most colourful fairyland of the Thousand and One Nights is
created by a slight rearrangement of the familiar material of everyday life. And upon reflection, when one examines them with more
precision, one finds the same to be true of the boldest and most
profound philosophical systems: If for the poet it was creation by
aid of intuitive pictures, so for the philosopher it is construction by

more abstract yet still familiar concepts, from which by apparently more transparent principles of combination new structures are formed.

The physicist, too, at first proceeds in much the same way in the construction of hypotheses. This is particularly indicated by the tenacity of the belief, held for many centuries by the physicist, that to explain nature a copy of its processes in models perceptible to the senses is necessary. Thus, for instance, he repeatedly attributed characteristics of visible, tangible substances to the ether without the slightest reason for doing so. Only when observed facts either suggest or necessitate his use of the new systems of concepts does the physicist realise the new possibilities and break himself free from his former habits of thought; but then he readily and with the greatest ease makes the jump to, say, Riemannian space or to Einsteinian time, to concepts so daring and profound that neither the imagination of the poet nor the intellect of the philosopher could have been able to anticipate them.

The turning point at which recent physics has arrived with respect to the question of *causality* could likewise not have been foreseen. Although there has been so much philosophising about determinism and indeterminism, about the content, validity, and mode of testing of the principle of causality, no one thought of precisely that possibility leading in quantum physics to the key that allows us a view of the real nature of the causal order. Only in retrospect do we realise how the new ideas differ from the old, and we are perhaps a little amazed that so far we have always missed the point. Now, however, after the significance of the concept of quantum theories has been demonstrated by the extraordinary results of its application, and we have had some years to accustom ourselves to the new ideas, it should not be premature to attempt to arrive at philosophical clarity as to the meaning and scope of the ideas that contemporary physics contributes to the problem of causality.

2. Causality and the Principle of Causality

The observation that philosophical meditations did not foresee possibilities that were found later on, because of their close adherence to existing ideas, is true also of the ideas I propounded more than ten years ago.[1] Still it is probably not useless to return to some points of those earlier considerations, since in this way the progress accomplished in the meantime becomes so much clearer.

First it is necessary to determine what the scientist actually means when he speaks of "causality." Where does he use this word? Obviously, wherever he supposes a "dependence" between certain events. (Nowadays it is self-evident that only events and not "things" come into question as elements of a causal relationship, since physics forms the four dimensional reality from events, and considers "things," three dimensional bodies, as mere abstractions.) But what does "dependence" mean? In science, in any case, it is always expressed by *a law;* causality is, accordingly, nothing but another word for the existence of a law. The content of the *principle* of causality then clearly lies in the assertion that *everything* in the world occurs according to laws; it is indifferent whether we affirm the validity of the principle of causality or of *determinism*. In order to formulate the principle of causality or the deterministic thesis, we must first have defined what is meant by a law of nature or by mutual "dependence" of natural events. For only when we know this are we able to understand the meaning of determinism, which states that *every* event is a member of a causal relation, that *every* process is wholly dependent upon other processes. (We shall not discuss whether the attempt to make a statement about "all" natural processes could lead to logical difficulties.)

Thus in any event we distinguish the question of the meaning of the word "causality" or "natural law" from the question of the validity of the principle of causality or the law of causality, and we concern ourselves at the beginning with the first question only.

The distinction we thus make coincides with that made by H. Reichenbach at the beginning of his essay "Die Kausalstruktur der Welt."[2] He speaks there of the difference between two "forms of the hypothesis of causality." He calls the first the "implication form." It is given "when physics establishes laws, that is, makes statements of the form: 'if A then B.'" The second is "the deterministic form of the causal hypothesis;"[3] it is identical with determinism, which

---

[1] *Naturwiss* (1920) , 461 ff.

[2] *Sitzungsber. Bayr. Akad. Wis., Math-Physik. Kl.* (1925) , 133.

[3] "Determinationsform der Kausalhypothese" in the original (trans.) .

states that the course of the world as a whole "remains unchangeable, that with a single cross section of the four dimensional world the past and future are fully determined." It seems to me simpler and more to the point to characterise the difference involved as the difference between the concept of causality and the principle of causality.

The question then concerns the content of the concept of causality. When do we say that a process A "determines" another B, that B "depends" upon A, that B is related to A by *law?* What do the words "if—then," indicating causal relationship, mean in the statement "if A then B?"

3. LAW AND ORDER

In the language of physics a natural process is represented as a sequence of values of definite physical magnitudes. We note already here that, of course, in a sequence only a finite number of values can be measured, that, therefore, experience affords only a discrete manifold of observed magnitudes, and further, that every value is conceived as subject to a certain inexactitude.

Assuming that a large number of such observed magnitudes are given, we then ask quite generally: How does such a number of values have to be constituted so that we may say that it represents a *law-like* sequence, that there is a causal relationship between the observed magnitudes? We may, to begin with, presuppose that the data already possesses a natural order, namely the spatio-temporal one; that is to say, each quantitative value relates to a definite position in space and time. It is of course true that only with the aid of causal considerations are we able to indicate the position of events in physical space-time, by passing from phenomenal space-time, which represents the natural order of our experiences, to the physical world. But this complication may be excluded in our considerations, which limit themselves entirely to the realm of the physical world. Furthermore, our considerations are based upon a most fundamental assumption which I here mention in passing only, since it has already been discussed in a previous work (loc. cit. p. 463) . It is the hypothesis that in nature there are certain "similarities," in the sense that different realms of nature are *comparable* to one another, so that we may say for instance: "the same" *magnitude* that in this place has value f_1 has the value f_2 in another place. Comparability is then one of the presuppositions of measurability. It is not easy to give the real meaning of this assumption, but we need not concern ourselves with it since this last analysis is likewise irrelevant to our problem.

According to these observations, our problem regarding the content of the concept of causality reduces itself to this: what characteristic must the spatio-temporally ordered group of values have so that it may be regarded as an expression of a "law of nature"? This characteristic can be nothing but an *order*, and indeed, since events extensive in space and time are already *orderly*, it must be a kind of *intensive* order. This order must be of the *temporal* sort, for, as is well known, we do not speak of causality in reference to spatial order (popularly expressed by "simultaneous," coexistent events) ; the concept of activity finds no application there. Spatial regularities, if such there be, would be called "coexistence laws."

After limiting ourselves to the time dimension we must, I believe, now say: *Every* order of events in time, of whatever kind, is to be regarded as a causal relationship. Only complete chaos, complete irregularity, is to be designated as an acausal occurrence, as pure chance; every trace of an order would mean dependence, therefore causality. I believe that this use of the word "causal" is closer to its everyday sense than when confined, as seems to be done by many natural philosophers, to such an order as we could designate by "complete causality"—by which phrase it appears that something like "complete determination" of the event in question is meant (of course, we can express ourselves here in inexact terms only). If we should restrict the word to complete causality, we run the danger of finding no use at all for it in nature, while *in some sense* we do regard the existence of causality as a fact of experience. And there would be even less reason to place the boundary between law and chance at some other point.

The only alternative that confronts us is thus: order or disorder? Causality and law are identical with order; irregularity and chance are identical with disorder.

The result up to the present therefore seems to be: we call a natural process, described by a group of values, causal or regular if the values show any temporal order whatever. This definition becomes meaningful only when we know what is to be understood by "order," how it differs from chaos. A most puzzling problem!

4. ATTEMPTS AT DEFINITION OF REGULARITY

It is certain that in our daily life as well as in science we differentiate rather clearly between order and disorder, regularity and irregularity. How are we to understand this? At first glance the answer does not seem very difficult. It appears that we need only make sure how physics actually represents laws of nature, in which form it describes the dependence of events. Now, this form is the mathematical *function*. The dependence of one event upon another is expressed by the fact that the values of apart of the magnitudes are represented as functions of the others. Every order of numbers is mathematically represented by a function; and so it appears as if the desired criterion of order, which differentiates it from disorder, is expressibility by a function.

But as soon as the idea of the identity of function and law is expressed, we see that it cannot possibly be correct. For, as is well-known, whatever be the distribution of given magnitudes, functions may *always* be found that represent just that distribution with any degree of accuracy; and this means that every possible distribution of magnitudes, every conceivable series of values is to be considered as an order. There would be no chaos.

Thus we do not in this way successfully distinguish causality from chance, order from disorder, or succeed in defining rule and law in this manner. As was shown also in our previous considerations, there seems to remain only the alternative of imposing certain requirements on the functions that describe the observed series of values, and by means of them to determine the concept of order. We should then have to say: if the functions that describe the distribution of values of the magnitudes have such and such a definite structure, the represented sequence is in accordance with law, otherwise it is unordered.

Thereby we find ourselves in a rather hopeless situation, for it is clear that in this way arbitrariness is given free rein, and a distinction between law and chance resting upon such an arbitrary basis could never be satisfactory. It could be so only if a fundamental and sharp distinction in the structure of the functions could be ascertained, which at the same time possessed such definite empirical possibilities of application that everyone would immediately recognise them as the correct formulation of the concepts of regularity and irregularity as they are applied in science.

Here there appear simultaneously two ways, both of which men have tried to adopt. The first was already used by Maxwell to define causality. It consists of the following stipulation: the space and time co-ordinates are not to appear explicitly in the equations that describe the sequence in question. This requirement is equivalent to the notion popularly expressed in the phrase: similar causes, similar effects. In fact it means that a process that takes place anywhere and any time in a definite manner will take place in exactly the same manner in every other place and time, under the same circumstances. In other words, the rule states the *universal validity* of the relationship represented. Universal validity, however, is, as has been generally acknowledged, exactly that which in laws of nature has been designated by the ambiguous term "necessity," so that it appears as if the essential nature of the causal relation had been correctly hit upon by this stipulation.

Concerning Maxwell's definition of law, which I myself previously defended (in the passage cited) , we may say the following:

The concept of law in physics is undoubtedly such that this requirement is always fulfilled. Actually no investigator thinks of formulating laws of nature that refer explicitly to definite positions and moments in the universe. If space and time occurred explicitly in the physical equations, they would have quite a different significance from the one they actually have in our world. The relativity of space and time, fundamental to our world-view, would be denied, and time and space could no longer assume the peculiar role of "forms" of occurrence which they have in our cosmos. We should therefore be free to maintain the Maxwellian condition of causality—would it, however, be a necessary condition? We shall hardly be allowed to say that, for surely a world is conceivable in which all events would have to be expressed in formulas in which space and time appear explicitly, without our denying that these formulas represent true laws and that this world is completely orderly. So far as I can see, it would be conceivable, for instance, that uniform measurements of the elementary quantum of electricity (electric charge) would give values for these magnitudes that would fluctuate about 5 per cent in seven hours and then again in seven hours, and then ten hours, without our being able to find the slightest "reason" for it. And besides that, perhaps still another variation might appear for which we would make an absolute change of position of the earth in space responsible. In this case then the Maxwellian condition would not be fulfilled, but we would surely not find the world to be disorderly and we would formulate its regularity and be able to make predictions by means of it. We shall therefore be inclined to the view that the Maxwellian definition is too limited, and we shall ask ourselves what the criterion of law would be in the hypothetical case we have discussed.

Now, the decisive factor of the hypothetical case seems to be that we could so easily consider the influence of space and time, that they enter into the formulas in such a *simple* manner. If, in our example, the electric charge were to behave differently every week and every hour, or form a completely "irregular curve," we could of course afterwards represent its dependence upon time by a function, but this function would be very complicated. We would then say that no law exists but that the variations of magnitudes are governed by "chance." We do not have to invent cases of this kind since, as is well known, the new physics accepts them as commonplace. The discontinuous events in the atom that Bohr's theory interpreted as jumps of an electron from one orbit into another are regarded as purely accidental, as "acausal," although we may subsequently think of their occurrence as a function of time. But this function would be very complicated, not periodic, not readily grasped, and it is for this reason only that we say that no regularity exists. But as soon as any simple statement regarding the jumps is formulable—if, for instance, the time intervals become increasingly larger—this would at once appear to us as a regularity, even though time would explicitly enter into the formula.

Accordingly, it appears as if we speak of order, law, causality when the course of events is described by functions of *simple* form; while complexity of the formula is the criterion for disorder, lawlessness, chance. And so one very easily arrives at the point of defining causality by the *simplicity* of the descriptive functions. Simplicity is, however, a half pragmatic, half aesthetic concept. We may therefore call this definition aesthetic. Also, without being able to state what is here meant by "simplicity," we must yet affirm the fact that every investigator who has succeeded in representing a series of observations in a simple formula (for instance, linear, quadratic, exponential function) is quite sure of having discovered a *law*, and so the aesthetic definition, as well as the Maxwellian one, obviously discloses a characteristic of causality that is considered a decisive criterion. Which of the two attempts at formulating the concept of law shall we accept? Or shall we formulate a new definition by combining both?

5. INADEQUACY OF THE ATTEMPTS AT DEFINITION

To sum up: the Maxwellian definition has *in its favour* the fact that all known laws of nature satisfy it, and that it may be considered to be an adequate expression of the proposition, "similar causes, similar effects." *Against* this definition is the fact that cases are *conceivable* in which we should certainly acknowledge regularity without the fulfillment of the criterion.

The "aesthetic" definition has *in its favour* that it is also applicable to the above considered cases, to which the other one is not, and that also undoubtedly in the prosecution of science "simplicity" of functions is used as a criterion of order and law. *Against* it, however, is the fact that simplicity is clearly a relative and indefinite concept, so that a strict definition of causality is not obtained, and law and chance cannot be sufficiently distinguished. It might indeed be possible that we have to take this last idea into account, and that a "law of nature" is actually not something so precisely conceivable as one might at first think; however, such a point of view will be accepted only when one is sure that no other possibility remains.

It is certain that the concept of simplicity can only be fixed by a convention that must always remain arbitrary. We should probably be inclined to consider a function of the first degree simpler than a function of the second degree; however, even the latter undoubtedly represents an unexceptionable law when it describes the data of observation with great accuracy. The Newtonian formula of gravitation, in which the square of the distance occurs, is generally still regarded as a paradigm case of a simple natural law. One may, for example, agree further that of all continuous curves that pass through a given number of points with sufficient proximity, we may consider as simplest the one that everywhere on the average has the greatest radius of curvature. (There is an unpublished work on this by Marcel Natkin.) However, such artifices seem unnatural, and the fact alone that there are *degrees* of simplicity makes the definition of causality based upon it unsatisfactory.

This state of affairs is made even worse by the fact that, as we know, it is not at all a matter of the simplicity of an isolated law, but of the simplicity of the system of all natural laws. And so, for instance, the true equation of the law of gases has by no means the simple form given to it by Boyle-Mariotte; yet we know that its complicated form may be explained by a particularly simple set of elementary laws. In principle it should be much more difficult to find rules for the simplicity of a *system* of formulas. They would always remain provisional, so that apparent order could with progressive knowledge turn out to be disorder.

And so neither the Maxwellian nor the aesthetic criterion seems to give a really satisfactory answer to the question as to what causality actually is. The first seems too narrow, the second too vague. No progress in principle is made by a combination of both attempts, and one may readily see that the shortcomings cannot be removed by improvements along the same lines. The shortcomings observed are clearly of a fundamental nature, and that gives us the idea of revising the present point of departure and of considering whether we are in general on the right path.

6. PREDICTION AS CRITERION OF CAUSALITY

Until now we have assumed that a definite distribution of values is given, and asked: when does it represent a regular and when a chance sequence? It may be that this question cannot be answered at all by mere consideration of the distribution of values, but that it is necessary to go beyond this domain.

Let us for a moment consider the consequences that the statements made about the *concept* of causality have for the *principle* of causality. We imagine that for as many internal and boundary points of a physical system as possible we attempt to determine the value of the state variables by precise observation. Now one is in the habit of saying that the principle of causality is valid if from the state of the system during a very short time and from the boundary conditions all other states of the system may be deduced. Such a deduction is, however, possible *under all circumstances,* for according to what has been said, functions may always be found that represent all observed values with any desired accuracy. And as soon as we have such functions we may by means of them compute all states *already observed,* whether earlier or later, from any state of the system. For functions have been chosen in such a way that they represent everything observed in the system. In other words: the principle of causality would be satisfied *under all circumstances.* A statement, however, that is applicable to any system whatever, no matter what its properties, says nothing at all about this system, is an *empty* statement, a mere tautology, and it is futile to construct it. Hence if the causal law is actually to mean something, if it has content, the formulation from which we began must be false, for the law has turned out to be tautological. If, however, we make the qualification that the equations used are not to contain the space and time co-ordinates explicitly, or that they are to be very "simple," the principle acquires, to be sure, a real content; but, in the first case the reflection is valid that we have formulated too limited a concept of causality, and in the second the sole characteristic would be that the computation would be easier. However, we should certainly not want to formulate the difference between chaos and order in such manner that we say the first is comprehensible only to an excellent mathematician, the second to an average one.

We must therefore begin anew and attempt to formulate the meaning of the causal law differently. Our error until now was that we did not conform with enough precision to the actual procedure by which, in science, one actually tests whether processes are or are not dependent upon one another, whether or not a law, a causal sequence, exists. Until now we only investigated how a law is *constructed.* To learn its real meaning, however, one must observe how it is *tested.* It is always the case that the significance of a statement is revealed only by the manner of its verification. How then is the test made?

After we have succeeded in finding a function that satisfactorily connects a group of observational data, we are by no means satisfied, even when the function found has a very simple structure, for now comes the main thing, which our considerations hitherto have not touched: We observe whether the formula obtained also represents correctly those observations that *were not used* in achieving the formula. For the physicist, as an investigator of reality, the only important, decisive, and essential thing is that equations derived from certain data be applicable to other, *new* data. Only when this is true does he consider his formula to be a law. In other words, the true criterion of law, the essential sign of causality, is the *success of prediction*.

By success of prediction is to be understood, according to what has been said, nothing but the confirmation of a formula for such data as have not been used in its construction. Whether these data have already been observed or are only subsequently determined is in this connection of no consequence whatever. This observation is of great importance: past and future data are altogether on the same footing in this respect, the future is not of special significance; the criterion of causality is not confirmation in the future but confirmation in general.

It is self-evident that the test of a law can occur only *after* its formulation, but this gives no special distinction to the future. What is essential is that it is indifferent whether the verifying data are in the past or the future; it is incidental when they become known or are used for verification. The confirmation remains the same whether the data were known before the formulation of a theory, as in the case of the anomaly of Mercury's movement, or whether it was prophesied by the theory, as in the case of the red-shift of the spectral lines. Only for the *application* of science, for technique, is it of fundamental importance that natural laws allow prediction of something new, observed by no one as yet. And so earlier philosophers, Bacon, Hume, Comte, have long known that knowledge of reality coincides with the possibility of prediction. Thus fundamentally they correctly formulated the essence of causality.

7. ELUCIDATION OF THE RESULT

If we accept the success of prediction as the true criterion of a causal relationship—and, with an important limitation to be mentioned presently, we shall have to do so—we thereby admit as well that the previous attempts at definition no longer enter into consideration. In fact, if we can really predict new observations, it does not matter how the formulas that enabled us to do so were constructed, whether they seem simple or complicated, whether time and space enter explicitly or not. As soon as someone can calculate the new observation data from the old, we shall admit that he has grasped the law governing the processes; prediction is therefore a sufficient characteristic of causality.

We easily realize that confirmation is also a necessary characteristic, and that the Maxwellian and aesthetic criteria do not suffice, when we imagine we have found a formula of great simplicity that describes a definite natural process with great precision but at once ceases to work when applied to the further phases of the process, to new observations. Obviously we should then say that the distribution of magnitudes occurring once has simulated a dependence of natural events which in reality does not exist, that it was a matter of mere chance the particular sequence could be described by simple formulas. That there was no natural law is proven by the fact that our formula can stand no test, for in the attempt to repeat the observations the sequence occurs quite differently; the formula is no longer applicable. A second alternative seems, of course, to be that one may say the law was valid at the time of the observation but no longer holds. It is clear, however, that this is only another way of expressing the absence of law, the universality of the law being denied. The "regularity" observed for the single sequence was not true regularity, but merely chance. The confirmation of prediction is therefore the *only* criterion of causality. Through it alone does reality speak to us; the construction of laws and formulas is simply the work of man.

Here I must include two observations that go together and are of basic importance. First, I said previously that we may recognise the "verification" of a regularity as the adequate characteristic of causality only subject to a limitation. This limitation consists in the fact that the confirmation of a prediction never actually *proves* the existence of causality but always only makes it *probable*. Further observations may indeed show the supposed law to be always incorrect, and then we should have to say that "it expressed the sequence only by chance." A final verification is therefore, so to say, impossible in principle. We deduce therefrom that a causal statement logically does not at all have the characteristic of a *proposition*, for a genuine proposition must in the end allow itself to be verified. We shall return to this shortly without, however, being able to explain this apparent paradox fully here, where we are not concerned with logic.

The second observation concerns the fact that between the criterion of confirmation and the two rejected attempts at definition a remarkable relationship exists nevertheless. It lies simply in the fact that *actually* the different characteristics go hand in hand. We certainly expect with great assurance that precisely those formulas satisfying the Maxwellian criterion and distinguished by aesthetic simplicity will be confirmed, and that the propositions made by their help will be true. And even if we should sometimes be disappointed in this expectation, the fact remains that the laws that have really proved to be valid were always of a profound simplicity, and always fulfilled the Maxwellian definition. But what the significance of this "simplicity" is, is difficult to say, and much erroneous thinking has been done in this connection; we do not wish to put too much stress upon it. It is certain that we may imagine much "simpler" worlds than our own. There is also a "simplicity" that is merely a matter of *representation*, that is, pertains to symbolism by means of which we express facts. Its consideration leads to the question of "conventionalism" and does not interest us in this connection.

At any rate we see that if a formula corresponds to both of the earlier and inadequate criteria we consider it probable that it is really the expression of a law, of an actually existing order, that it will therefore be *confirmed*. If it has been confirmed, we think it again probable that it will continue to be so. (And indeed, it is understood, without bringing in new hypotheses, for in general physical laws are so constructed that they may always be maintained by new hypotheses brought in *ad hoc*. But if these become too complicated, one says that the law nevertheless does not hold, the right order has not been found.) The word probability, which we use here, moreover designates something completely different from the concept treated in the calculus of probability and occurring in statistical physics.[4]

For the sake of logical clarity (for philosophers this is the prime concern) it is of greatest importance to realise the situation precisely. We have seen that, basically, causality is not at all definable in the sense that for an *already given* sequence one could answer the question: Was it causal or not? Only in reference to the *single case*, to the single verification, can one say: It behaves as causality demands. For advancement in knowledge of nature (and this is the main concern of the physicist) this is fortunately quite sufficient. If a few verifications—under some circumstances only one—are successful, we build practically on the verified law, with the unqualified reliance with which we trust our life to a motor constructed according to natural laws.

It has indeed been frequently observed that one cannot actually speak of an absolute verification of a law, since we always, so to say, silently reserve the right to modify it on the basis of further experience. If I may in passing add a few words about the logical situation, the circumstance mentioned means that basically a natural law does not have the logical character of a "proposition" but represents "a direction for the formulation of propositions." (I owe these ideas and terms to Ludwig Wittgenstein.) We have already indicated this, above, regarding causal statements, and actually a causal statement is identical with a law. The statement, "The principle of energy holds," for instance, says no more nor less about nature than the principle of energy itself says. As is well known, only the individual propositions derived from a natural law are testable, and these always have the form: "Under such and such circumstances this indicator will point to that mark on the scale," "Under such and such circumstances there occurs a darkening on this point of the photographic plate," and the like. The verifiable propositions are of this nature and of this nature is every verification.

[4] Cf. F. Waismann, "Logische Analyse des Wahrscheinlichkeitsbegriffs," *Erkenntnis* I, 238, with whose analysis I find myself in principle in full agreement.

Verification in general, the success of a prediction, confirmation in experience, is therefore the criterion of causality, simply; and indeed in the practical sense in which alone we may speak of the test of a law. In this sense, however, the question regarding the existence of causality *is* testable. That confirmation in experience, the success of a prediction, is something *final,* not subject to further analysis, cannot be over-emphasised. No number of propositions can state when it must occur, but we must simply await whether it occur or not.

8. CAUSALITY AND QUANTUM THEORY

In the previous considerations nothing was said except what, in my opinion, may be read out of the procedure of the scientist. No concept of causality was constructed; only the role it actually plays in physics was determined. Now the attitude of most physicists towards certain results of quantum theory shows that they see the essence of causality just where the foregoing considerations also found it, namely, in the possibility of *prediction.* When the physicists say that complete validity of the causal principle is not compatible with the quantum theory, the basis, indeed the *meaning,* of this assertion, lies simply in the fact that the theory makes precise *predictions* impossible. We must try to make this really clear to ourselves.

In contemporary physics it is possible to say, in a manner of speaking, that, with certain limitations to be mentioned, each physical system is to be considered as a system of protons and electrons, and that its state is completely determined by the position and momentum of its particles being known at every moment. Now, as is well known, a certain formula is derived from the quantum theory, the so-called "uncertainty principle" of Heisenberg, which teaches that it is impossible to indicate for a particle *both* determinants, place *and* velocity, with any desired precision, and that the more precise the value of one co-ordinate the greater inexactness we must expect for the other. If we know say that the place co-ordinate lies within a small interval Δp, the velocity co-ordinate q may be indicated only with such precision that its value remains undetermined in the interval Δq, and indeed so that the product Δp.

Δq is of the order of magnitude of Planck's quantum effect h. In principle then the one co-ordinate could be determined with any degree of precision, but absolutely precise observation of it will have as a consequence that we can say *nothing more* about the other co-ordinate.

This principle of indeterminacy has been so frequently illustrated, even in popular form, that we need not describe the situation any more closely; our task must be to understand exactly its real *meaning*. When we ask for the meaning of a statement this always means (not only in physics) : by which particular experiences do we test its truth? When thus, for example, we conceive the place of an electron to be determined by observation with an inexactness Δp, what does it mean when I say, for instance, the direction of the velocity of this electron may be indicated only with an inexactness $\Delta\theta$? How do I determine whether this statement is true or false?

Now, that a particle has gone in a definite direction may be tested only by its arrival at a definite point. To give the velocity of a particle *signifies* absolutely nothing more than to predict that in a certain time it will arrive at a certain point. "The inexactness of direction amounts to $\Delta\theta$" means: in a certain experiment I shall find the electron within the angle $\Delta\theta$; however, I do not know exactly *where* therein. And if I repeat "the same" experiment I shall find the electron at various points within the angle, and I never know *beforehand* at which point in it. If the position of the particle is observed with absolute precision the result would be that in principle we could not know at all in which direction the electron would be found after a short time. Only further observation could subsequently tell us this, and with very frequent repetition of "the same" experiment it must appear that on the average no one direction predominates.

The fact that both position and velocity of an electron cannot be precisely measured is usually interpreted as saying: it would be impossible to describe fully the state of a system at a definite point in time, and therefore the principle of causality becomes inapplicable. Since the principle asserts that the future states of the system are determined by its initial state, since, thus, it presupposes that the initial state may be described in principle exactly, the principle of causality collapses, for this presupposition has not been fulfilled. I should not like to call this idea false, but it seems useless to me, because it does not express the essential point clearly. What is essential is that one realise that the indeterminacy that the Heisenberg-relation expresses is in truth an indeterminacy of *prediction*.

In principle nothing interferes (this is also emphasised by Eddington in a similar thought context) with our determining the position of an electron twice at any two closely adjacent points in time, and with our considering these measurements equivalent to position and velocity measurements. But the vital point is that with data about a state obtained in such a manner we are never in a position to predict a future state with precision. If, that is, we should define the velocity of the electron in the usual manner (distance divided by time) by means of the observed places and times, the velocity would nevertheless be different in the next moment, for, as we know, it must be assumed that its course is disturbed by observation in a quite uncontrollable manner. This alone is the true significance of the statement that a momentary state is not precisely determinable; that is, the impossibility of prediction alone is the actual reason why the physicist deems necessary the denial of causality.

There is no doubt, therefore, that quantum physics finds the criterion of causality precisely where we too have discovered it, and speaks of the failure of the principle of causality only because it has become impossible to make predictions with any desired degree of accuracy. I cite M. Born, *Naturwiss.* 17 (1929) :

> The impossibility of measuring exactly all the data of a state prevents the predetermination of its further course of development. Because of this principle of causality in its usual formulation loses all significance. For when it is impossible in principle to know all the conditions (causes) of an event, it is empty talk to say that every event has a cause.

Causality as such, the existence of laws, is however not denied. There are still valid predictions, but they do not consist in the expression of exact magnitude values, but are of the form: the magnitude X will lie in the interval between a and Δa.

What is new in the contribution of the most recent physics to the problem of causality does not consist in the fact that the validity of the causal principle is contested at all, nor that, say, the micro-structure of nature is described by statistical rather than causal regularities, nor in the fact that the realisation of the merely probable validity of natural laws has displaced belief in their absolute validity. All these ideas have, in part, long since been expressed. The novelty rather consists in the hitherto unsuspected discovery that through natural laws themselves a limit is set in principle to precision in predictions. That is something quite different from the rather obvious idea that actually and practically there is a limit to precision in observations and that the assumption of absolutely precise natural laws is in every case unnecessary if one wants to give an account of every experience. Previously it must always have seemed as if the question of determinism had to remain undecided in principle. The kind of decision now available, namely, by means of a natural law itself (the Heisenberg relation), was not foreseen. In any case, one who today speaks of a decidability and holds the question to be answered unfavorably for determinism must assume that law of nature as actually existing and raised beyond all doubt. That we are absolutely sure of this, or ever could be, a careful investigator will hesitate to state. But the principle of indeterminacy is an integral part of the structure of the quantum theory, and we must trust its correctness so long as new experiments and new observations do not force us to revise the quantum theory. (In fact it is daily better confirmed.) But to have shown that a theory of such structure is at all possible in the description of nature is in itself a great accomplishment of modern physics. It signifies an important philosophical clarification of the basic concepts of natural science. The progress in principle is clear. One may now speak of an empirical test of the principle of causality *in the same sense* as of the test of some special law of nature. And that we may in some sense justifiably speak of it is proven simply by the existence of science.

9. IS THE PRINCIPAL OF CAUSALITY IN THE QUANTUM THEORY FALSE OR EMPTY?

In order to understand the situation it is necessary to compare two formulations that the criticism of the causal principle assumes in physics. Some say that the quantum theory has shown (of course presupposing that it is correct in its present form) that the principle is *not valid* in nature. The others say that it is *empty*. The former believe thus that it makes a definite assertion about reality that experience has proven false; the others believe that the proposition in which it is apparently expressed is not at all a genuine assertion but is a meaningless succession of words.

As evidence for the first point of view, Heisenberg's oft cited article (in Z. *Physik, 1927,* 43) is quoted, which says: "Because all experiments are subject to the laws of quantum mechanics, the invalidity of the causal law is definitively determined by quantum mechanics." Born is commonly named as representing the second point of view (cf. the passage cited above). Hugo Bergmann ("Der Kampf um das Kausalgesetz in der jüngsten Physik," Braunschweig, 1929) and Thilo Vogel ("Zur Erkenntnistheorie der quantentheoretischen Grundbegriffe" Diss., Giessen, 1929) have concerned themselves with the philosophical aspects of this dilemma. Both of these authors correctly assume that those physicists who reject the causal principle are none the less of the same opinion basically, even if they say different things, and that the apparent difference is to be attributed to the inexact language of the one party. Both are of the opinion that it is Heisenberg who is guilty of the inexactness, and that therefore it should not be said that the quantum theory has proven the principle to be *false*. Both emphasize the fact that the causal law can neither be affirmed nor rejected by experience. Shall we consider this interpretation as correct?

First we must affirm that we consider the bases upon which H. Bergmann forms his opinion to be quite incorrect. For him the causal law is to be neither discredited nor affirmed, because he considers it to be a synthetic judgment *a priori* in the *Kantian* sense. On the one hand, as is well known, such a judgment is supposed to express a genuine cognition (this is conveyed by the word "synthetic"), on the other hand it must be incapable of test by experience because "the possibility of experience" rests upon it (that is conveyed by the words *a priori*). We know today that these two requirements contradict each other; there are no synthetic judgments *a priori*. If a proposition says anything at all about reality (and only when it does so does it contain knowledge) its truth or falsity must be determinable by observation of reality. If there is no possibility of such a test *in principle,* if the proposition is compatible with every experience, it must be empty and cannot contain any knowledge of nature. If, on the assumption of the falsity of the proposition, something in the world of experience were different from what it would be if the proposition were true, then of course it could be tested. Consequently not-testable-through-experience means that the way the world appears to us is quite independent of the truth or falsity of the proposition, hence it says nothing about the world. Kant, of course, believed that the principle of causality says a great deal about the empirical world, even determines its essential nature. Therefore one does no favour to Kantianism or *a-priorism* when one affirms that the principle cannot be tested. With this we have rejected H. Bergmann's point of view (the same would hold true of Th. Vogel's opinion in so far as he inclines towards a moderated, *a priorism;* however his formulations at the end of the treatise cited are not quite clear to me) and we must therefore consider a new phase of the question. Does the falsity of the principle of causality really follow from results of quantum mechanics? Or does it follow rather that the proposition is without content?

A sequence of words may be meaningless in two ways: either it is tautological (empty) or it is not a proposition at all, not an assertion in the logical sense. It would appear at first sight as if the latter possibility did not enter into our considerations here, for if the words that are to express the causal principle do not represent a real proposition, they must simply be a meaningless, absurd succession of words. One must, however, bear in mind that there are sequences of words that are not propositions and express no facts and yet fulfil very significant functions in life; so-called *question* and *command* sentences. And even if the causal principle is expressed in the grammatical form of a declarative sentence, we know from modern logic that one can hardly judge the logical content of a sentence by its form. And thus it is quite possible that beneath the categorical form of the causal principle a kind of command, a demand exists— thus, approximately, what Kant calls a "regulative principle." A similar opinion regarding this principle is indeed held by those philosophers who see in it merely the expression of a postulate or of a "decision"[5] never to give up the quest for laws and causes. This point of view therefore must be carefully considered.

Accordingly, we must decide between the following three possibilities:

I. The principle of causality is a tautology. In this case it would always be true but without content.

II. It is an empirical proposition. In this case it could be either true or false, either knowledge or error.

III. It represents a postulate, an injunction to continue to seek causes. In this case it cannot be either true or false but is at most either appropriate or inappropriate.

I. We shall soon become clear regarding the first possibility, especially as we have already mentioned it above (§6). We found that the causal principle as expressed in the form, "All events occur according to law," is certainly tautological if by lawfulness is meant, "representable by some formula or other." From this, however, we inferred that this could not be the true content of the principle, and we looked for a new formulation. In fact, science in principle has no interest in a tautological proposition. If the causal principle were of this nature, determinism would be self-evident, but empty. And indeterminism, its opposite, would be self-contradictory, for the negation of a tautology is a contradiction. The question as to which one of the two is correct could not be raised at all. Therefore if modern physics not only formulates the question but believes it to be definitely answered by experience, what physics means by determinism and the principle of causality surely cannot be a tautology. In order to know whether a proposition is tautological or not one obviously needs no experience at all, one need only realise its meaning. If one should say that physics has demonstrated the tautological nature of the causal principle, it would be as senseless as to say that astronomy has shown that 2 times 2 equals 4.

Since the time of Poincaré, we have learned to note that apparently certain general statements enter into a description of nature which are not subject to confirmation or disproval, namely the "conventions." The genuine conventions, which are actually a type

---

[5] H. Gomperz, *Das Problem der Willensfreiheit* (1907).

of definition, must in fact be formulated as tautologies. Here, however, it is not necessary to go further into this matter. We conclude only that since we have already admitted that modern physics at any rate teaches us something about the validity of the principle of causality, it cannot be an empty proposition, a tautology, a convention; but it must be of such a nature that in some way it is subject to the judgment of experience.

II. Is the principle of causality simply a proposition the truth or falsity of which may be determined by observation of nature? Our previous considerations seem to support this interpretation. If it is correct we shall have to side with Heisenberg, therefore, in opposition to H. Bergmann and Th. Vogel in the above mentioned apparent opposition between the formulations of Heisenberg and Born, in which these investigators express the results of the quantum theory. I call that opposition apparent, for while Heisenberg speaks of the invalidity and Born of the senselessness of the causal principle, Born yet adds "in its usual formulation." Therefore it may well be that the usual formulation gives rise to nothing but a tautology, but that the real meaning of the principle could be formulated in a genuine statement which could be proven false by quantum experiments. In order to determine this we must again consider which formulation of the causal principle we found ourselves driven to accept. According to our former statements the content of the principle may be expressed thus: "All events are in principle predictable." If this statement were a genuine proposition it would be verifiable—and not only this, but we would be able to say that the verification has been attempted and has so far given a negative result.

But what is the case with our principle? Can the meaning of the word "predictable" be clearly indicated? We called an event "predicted" when it was deduced by the help of a formula that was constructed on the basis of a series of observations of other events. Mathematically expressed, prediction is an extrapolation. The denial of exact predictability, as the quantum theory teaches, would mean then that it is impossible to derive from a series of observations a formula that will also represent, exactly, *new* observation data. But what again does this "impossible" mean? One may, as we saw, *subsequently* always find a function that includes the new as well as the old data. A rule may, therefore, always be found that connects the previous data with the new data and makes both appear derivative from the same natural regularity. That impossibility is therefore not a *logical* one; it does not mean that *there is no* formula with the desired properties. Strictly speaking, however, it is also not a real impossibility; for it is possible that someone should by mere chance, by pure guess, always get the correct formula. No natural law prevents correct guesses regarding the future. No, that impossibility means that it is impossible to *seek* that formula, that is, there is no *rule* for obtaining such a formula. This, however, cannot be expressed in a legitimate proposition.

Our efforts to find a testable proposition equivalent to the causal principle have therefore failed. Our attempts at formulations have led only to pseudo-propositions. This result is not entirely unexpected, however, for we have already said that the causal principle may be tested for its correctness *in the same sense* that a natural law may be tested. We also noted, however, that natural laws, strictly analysed, are not propositions that are true or false, but are, rather, "directions" for the construction of such propositions. If this holds also of the causal principle, we find ourselves referred to the third possibility:

III. The principle of causality does not directly express a fact to us, say, about the regularity of the world, but it constitutes an imperative, a precept to seek regularity, to describe events by laws. Such a direction is not true or false but is good or bad, useful or useless. And what quantum physics teaches us is just this: that the principle is *bad,* useless, impracticable within the limits precisely laid down by the principle of indeterminacy. Within those limits it is impossible to seek for causes. Quantum mechanics actually teaches us this, and thus gives us a guiding thread to the activity that is called investigation of nature, an opposing rule against the causal principle.

Here one sees again how much the situation created by physics is different from the possibilities that have been thought out by philosophy. The causal principle is no *postulate* in the sense in which this concept occurs in earlier philosophers, for there it means a rule to which we must adhere *under all circumstances.* Experience, however, decides upon the causal principle, of course, not upon its truth or falsity—that would be senseless—but upon its utility. And natural laws themselves decide the limits of utility. In this lies the novelty of the situation. There are no postulates in the sense of the older philosophy. Each postulate may be limited by an opposing rule taken from experience, that is, may be recognised as inappropriate and thus nullified.

One might perhaps believe that this point of view would lead to a type of pragmatism, since the validity of natural laws and of causality depends only on their *confirmation* and on nothing else. But here there is a big difference that must be sharply emphasised. The statement of pragmatism that the truth of propositions consists entirely in their confirmation, in their usefulness, must from our standpoint be rejected. Truth and confirmation are not identical for us. On the contrary, since in the case of the causal principle we may test only its confirmation, only the usefulness of its precept, we may not speak of its "truth," and we deny to it the nature of a genuine statement. Of course, pragmatism may be understood psychologically and its teaching may, as it were, be excused, by saying that it is really difficult and requires thorough reflection to see the difference between a true proposition and useful rule, between a false proposition and useless rule. For "directions" of this type occur grammatically in the form of ordinary propositions.

While for a real assertion it is essential that it be in principle verifiable or falsifiable, the usefulness of a direction can never be absolutely proven because later observations may still prove it to be inappropriate. The Heisenberg relation itself expresses a natural law, and as such has the nature of a direction. On this basis alone the rejection of determinism arising therefrom cannot be considered proof of the falsity of a definite proposition, but may be considered only an indication of the inadequacy of a rule. The hope therefore always remains that with further knowledge the causal principle will again triumph.

The expert will observe that by considerations such as the above the so-called problem of "induction," too, ceases to have application, and is thus solved in the way in which Hume solved it. For the problem of induction consists in the question of the logical justification of general propositions regarding reality, which are always extrapolations from individual observations. We recognise, as

Hume does, that there is no logical justification for them; there cannot be one because they are not real propositions. Natural laws are not (in the logician's language) "general implications," because they cannot be verified for *all* cases, but are rules, instructions, aiding the investigator to find his way about in reality, to discover true propositions, to expect certain events. This expectation, this practical attitude, is what Hume expresses by the word "belief." We must not forget that observation and experimentation are *actions* by which we come into direct contact with nature. The relations between reality and us are sometimes expressed in sentences that have the grammatical form of propositions, but whose real meaning lies in their being directives for possible action.

To sum up: The rejection of determinism by modern physics means neither the falsity nor the emptiness of a definite proposition about nature, but the uselessness of the rule that, as the "causal principle," points the way to every induction and every natural law. And in fact the inapplicability of the rule is asserted only for a definitely circumscribed realm; there, however, with all the certainty that pertains to investigation in the exact physical sciences.

10. Order, Disorder, and "Statistical Regularity"

After the peculiar nature of the causal principle has become clear to us, we may now also understand the role actually played by the previously discussed, but then rejected, criterion of *simplicity*. It had to be rejected only in so far as it does not accord with the concept of cause. However we noticed that *de facto* it coincides with the true criterion, that of *confirmation*. For it clearly represents the special precept fruitful in our world, by which the general injunction of the causal principle, to seek regularity, is supplemented and perfected. The causal principle directs us to construct, from given observations, functions that lead to prediction of new ones. The principle of simplicity gives us the practical method by which we follow this direction, by saying: Connect the observation data by the "simplest" curve—which will then represent the function sought.

The causal principle could remain valid even if the rule, leading to success, were quite different. Therefore this rule does not suffice to determine the causal concept, but merely represents a narrower, more special application. As a matter of fact it often does not suffice to attain the correct extrapolation. If we thus recognise the purely practical nature of the principle of simplicity, it becomes clear that "simplicity" is not to be strictly defined. Here, however, the vagueness does not matter.

If, say, we should draw the simplest curve through the points representing data of the quantum processes in some experiment (for instance electronic jumps in the atom) it will be of no use in making predictions. *And since we know of no other rule* by which this aim would be realised, we say that the processes follow *no* law but are *accidental. De facto,* however, there does exist a marked concordance between simplicity and lawfulness, between chance and complexity. This leads us to an important consideration.

It is conceivable that extrapolation with the help of the simplest curve would almost always lead to the correct result; that, however, with no ascertainable reason now and then some single observation will not match in the prediction. In order to make the idea firm let us imagine the following simple case: By means of a very long series of observations in nature we determine that in 99 per cent of the cases, an event A is followed by an event B; but not in the remaining (irregular distributed) 1 per cent—without it being possible to find the slightest "cause" for the exception. We would say of such a world that it is still quite orderly, since our prophecies would be fulfilled on the average of 99 per cent (therefore much better than at present in meteorology or in many phases of medicine). We should therefore ascribe to this world causality, though of an "imperfect" sort. Every time that A occurs we shall expect the occurrence of B with great confidence; we shall rely upon it and get along not at all badly. Let us assume that the world otherwise is quite intelligible. If, then, with the best methods and the greatest efforts, science cannot account for the average 1 per cent deviation we shall finally rest content with that, and shall explain the world as orderly within limits. In such a case we have a "statistical law" before us. It is important to observe that a law of this kind, wherever we encounter it in science, is as it were a result of two components, in that the incomplete or statistical causality is divided into strict law and chance, which are superimposed upon each other. In the above example we should say that it is a strict law that on the average B follows A, in 99 out of 100 cases and that the distribution of the 1 per cent of deviating cases over the whole is *completely* a matter of chance. An example from physics: in the kinetic theory of gases the laws according to which each particle moves are accepted as perfectly strict; but the distribution of single particles and their states are, however, assumed to be completely "random" at any given moment. From a combination of both hypotheses, then, the macroscopic laws of gases result (for instance Van der Waal's law of gases) as well as the imperfect regularity of the Brownian movement.

Thus in a scientific description of the process we separate a purely causal from a purely accidental part. For the former we construct a strict theory, and the latter we view in the statistical manner, that is, using "laws" of probability, which, however, are not actually laws but (as will be shown) represent the definition of the "accidental." In other words, we are not satisfied with a statistical law of the above form, but conceive it as a mixture of *strict* regularity and *complete* irregularity. Another example obviously occurs in the Schrödinger quantum mechanics (in the interpretation of Born). There the description of the processes is also split into two parts: into the strictly regular diffusion of the ψ waves, and in the occurrence of a particle or a quantum, which is simply accidental, within the limits of "probability" determined by the ψ value at the point concerned. (That is, the value of ψ tells us, for instance, that at a definite point *on the average* 1,000 quanta per second enter. These 1,000, however, show quite an irregular distribution in themselves.)

What does "simply accidental" or "chance" or "completely unordered" mean here? From the previous case, of the regular occurrence of A and B together in an average of 99 per cent of the observations, which does not represent complete order, we may by gradual transitions pass to disorder. Let us assume, say, that observation shows that on the average the process B follows the process A in 50 per cent of the cases, the process C follows A in 40 per cent, and D follows A in the remaining 10 per cent. We should still speak of a definite regularity, of statistical causality, but we should then judge a much smaller degree of order to be present than in the first case. (A metaphysician would perhaps say that the process A has a certain "tendency" to call forth the process B, a slighter tendency toward the process C, etc.) When would we state that there is *no kind* of regularity, that therefore the events, A, B, C, D are completely independent on one another (in which case the metaphysician would say that there is no inherent tendency in A to produce its consequent) ?

Obviously only when, after a very long sequence of observations every series formed out of the different events by permutation (with repetition) occurs on the average with the same frequency (where the series would have to be small with respect to the whole sequence of observations). We should then say that nature has no predilection for a definite succession of processes, that the succession therefore takes place quite irregularly. Such a distribution of the events has usually been called a distribution "according to the rules of probability." Where such a distribution exists we speak of complete independence of the events in question; we say they are not causally connected with one another. And according to what has been said, this manner of speech does not signify merely an *indication* of the lack of regularity but is *identical* with it by definition. The so-called "probability distribution" is simply the *definition* of complete disorder, pure chance. It seems to be generally admitted that to speak of "laws of chance" is a very poor way of expressing the matter (since chance means the exact opposite of law). One too easily tends to ask the meaningless question (the so-called "problem of application" relates to this) how it happens that even chance is subject to law. I cannot therefore accept Reichenbach's point of view when he speaks of a "principle of distribution according to the law of probability" as a presupposition of all the natural sciences; which principle, along with the principle of causality, is to form the basis of all physical knowledge. That principle, he thinks, consists in the assumption that the irrelevant factors in a causal relationship, the "remaining factors," "exert their influence in accordance with the law of probability."[6] It seems to me that these "laws of probability" are nothing more than the *definition* of causal independence.

Of course we must here include an observation that although

6 "Kausalstruktur der Welt," p. 134.

without practical significance is yet of great importance, logically as well as in principle. The above definition of absolute disorder (equi-frequent average occurrence of all possible sequences of events) would be correct only in the case of an infinite number of observations. For it must be valid for series of any magnitude and every one of these must, according to the previous observation, be regardable as small in comparison with the total number of cases, that is, the total number of cases must surpass all limits. Since in reality this, of course, is impossible, we cannot, strictly speaking, decide *whether* disorder conclusively exists in any case. That this must be so follows, moreover, from our previous result, that for an already given sequence we cannot decide whether it is "orderly" or not. The same difficulty of principle exists here that makes it impossible to define the probability of any event in nature by the relative frequency of its occurrence. To arrive at correct estimates such as are required for mathematical computation (probability *calculations*) we should have to pass to the limit for an infinite number of cases—naturally a senseless demand for empiricism. This is often not sufficient considered.[7] The only useful method of defining probabilities is the one of *Spielraüme*, logical range (Bolzano, V. Kries, Wittgenstein, Waismann; see the above cited article of Waismann) .

This, however, does not belong to our theme. We now proceed to derive some consequences from the above considerations and to criticise others that are drawn here and there in this connection.

11. WHAT DOES "DETERMINED" MEAN?

Since, generally, we speak of causality by saying that one process *determines* another, that the future is *determined* by the present, we want once more to clarify for ourselves the true significance of this unhappy word "determine." That a certain state determines another later one can in the first place *not* mean that there is a hidden connection between them called causality, which could somehow be found or must be thought. For such naïve ways of thinking are, for us, surely no longer possible, 200 years after Hume.

---

[7] Cf. for instance R. von Mises, *Wahrscheinlichkeit, Statisik und Wahrheit* (1928) ; English translation: *Probability, Statistics and Truth* (1939) .

Now we have already given the positive answer, at the beginning of our deliberations: "A determines B" cannot mean anything but: B may be *calculated* from A. And this again means: there is a general formula which describes the state B as soon as certain values of the "initial state" A are put into it, and as soon as a certain value is given to certain variables, for instance that of time, t. That the formula is "general" means, again, that besides A and B there are any number of other states connected with one another by the same formula and in the same manner. Indeed a large part of our efforts was directed to answering the question of when one may say there *is* such a formula (called "natural law"). And the answer was that the criterion lay in nothing but the actual observation of the B computed from A. Only when we can indicate a formula that is used successfully in prediction can we say that there *is* a formula (order is present).

The word "determined" therefore means exactly the same as "predictable" or "computable in advance." This simple viewpoint alone is needed to resolve a well-known paradox, important for the problem of causality, which perplexed Aristotle and is even today a source of confusion. It is the paradox of so-called "logical determinism." It states that the principles of contradiction and of excluded middle would not be valid for propositions regarding future facts if determinism is not valid. In fact, so Aristotle argued, if indeterminism is correct, if the future is not already *determined,* it seems that the proposition, "the event E will take place the day after tomorrow," can be today neither true nor false. For if, for instance, it were true the event *would have to* occur, it would already be determined, contrary to the indeterministic assumption. Even in our day this argument is sometimes held to be conclusive, and is even said to be the basis of a new logic.[8] There must of course be an error here, for logical propositions, which are only rules of our symbolism, cannot depend as regards their validity upon the existence of causality in the world; every proposition must have truth or falsity as a timeless characteristic. The correct interpretation of determinism removes the difficulty at once and leaves to the logical principles

---

[8] Cf. J. Lukasiewicz, "Philosophische Bemerkungen zu mehrwertigen Systemen des Aussagenkalküls," *Comptes rendus des séances de la Société des Sciences et des Lettres de Varsovie* (1930) , 63 ff.

their validity. The proposition "the event E occurs on such and such a day" is timeless—therefore even now either true or false, and only one of the two, quite independently of whether determinism or indeterminism holds in the world. For the latter by no means asserts that today the proposition about the future E is not unambiguously true or false, but only that the truth or falsity of that proposition cannot be *calculated* on the basis of propositions about present events. This means, then, that we cannot *know* whether the proposition is true before the corresponding point in time has passed, but this has nothing to do with its being true or with the basic laws of logic.

12. Determination of the Past

If physics today, speaking indeterministically, says that the future is (within certain limits) *undetermined,* it means nothing more or less than: it is impossible to find a formula by which we may calculate the future from the present. (More correctly it would mean: it is impossible to *seek* such a formula, there is no rule for its discovery; it could be *guessed* only by pure chance.) It is perhaps comforting to observe that in quite the same sense (and I cannot imagine any other meaning of the word "undetermined") we must say of the past that in a certain respect it, too, is undetermined. Let us assume for example that the velocity of an electron has been precisely measured and then its location observed: in this case the equations of the quantum theory also enable us to compute, *exactly,* previous positions of the electron.[9] However, actually, this indication of position is physically meaningless, for its correctness cannot in principle be tested, since it is impossible to verify—subsequently—whether the electron appeared in the computed place at the given time. *If,* however, *one had* observed it in this computed place, it would certainly not have reached those places later noted, since its course is known to be disturbed by observation in an incalculable manner. Heisenberg says (p. 15) : "Whether or not one attributes a physical reality to the calculation of the past of the electron is merely a matter of taste." However, I should prefer

[9] Heisenberg also emphasises this: *Die Physikalischen Prinzipien der Quantentheorie* (1930) , p. 15.

to express myself even more strongly, in complete agreement with what I believe to be the fundamental point of view of Bohr and Heisenberg himself. If an assertion regarding the position of an electron is not verifiable in atomic dimensions, then we cannot attribute any meaning to it; it becomes impossible to speak of the "path" of a particle between two points where it has been observed. (This of course is not true of bodies of molar dimensions. If a bullet is now here and a second later at a distance of 10 metres, then it must have passed the points in between during that second, *even if no one has perceived it;* for in principle it is possible to verify subsequently that it has been at the intervening points.) One may treat this as the sharpened formulation of a proposition of the general theory of relativity: just as transformations that leave all point coincidences—intersection points of world lines—unchanged have no physical meaning, so we may say here, there is no sense at all in attributing physical reality to the segments of world-lines between the points of intersection.

The most concise description of the state of affairs we have discussed is perhaps to say (as the most important investigators of the quantum problems do) that the validity of the usual spatio-temporal concepts is limited to that which is macroscopically observable; they are not applicable to atomic dimensions.

None the less let us spend another moment with the results just arrived at concerning determination of the past. We sometimes find it asserted in current literature that contemporary physics has re-established the ancient Aristotelian concept of "final cause," in the form of that which is earlier being determined by the later, but not vice versa. This idea occurs in the interpretation of the formulas of atomic radiation which, according to the theory of Bohr, is supposed to take place so that the atom sends out a light quantum every time an electron jumps from a higher to a lower orbit. The frequency of the light quantum depends upon the initial orbit *and the final orbit* of the electron (it is proportional to the difference in energy values of the two orbits) ; it is therefore obviously determined by a *future* event (the entrance of the electron into the final orbit) .

Let us test the meaning of this idea. Aside from the fact that the concept of final cause must have had a different content for Aristotle, this idea, according to our analysis of "determine," states that in certain cases it is impossible to compute a future event Z from the data of past events V, but that, on the other hand, V may be derived from the known Z. Good, let us imagine that the formula for this is given and that a V has been computed therefrom. How do we test the correctness of the formula? Only by comparing that which is computed with the observed V. V, however, is already in the past (it existed before Z, which has also already occurred and had to be known in order to be insertable into the formula); it cannot be observed *post factum*. If then we have not previously ascertained it, the proposition that the computed V occurred is not verifiable in principle and is therefore meaningless. If however V has already been observed, we have a formula that connects events already observed. There is no reason why such a formula should not be reversible. (For in practice *one-many* functions do not occur in physics.) If by means of it V may be calculated from Z, it must be equally possible to determine Z by means of it when V is given. We therefore encounter a contradiction when we say the past may be calculated from the present but not vice versa. Logically both are the same. Note well: the essence of this argument is that the data of the events V and Z enter into the natural law with entirely equal right; they must all already have been observed if the formula is to be verifiable.

For the rest, here too, all the obscurities are basically due to the lack of clear distinction between that which may be formulated as a contribution of thought and that which has really been observed. Here again we see the great advantage of Heisenberg's point of view, which would offer a purely mathematical and not an apparently intuitive model of the atom; with it the temptation to introduce so-called "final causes" falls to the ground. It seems to me that the mere elucidation of the meaning of the word "determine" shows that it is under all circumstances impermissible to assume (quite independently of the question of determinism) that a later event determines an earlier one, but that the reverse is not true.

13. TOWARD DIFFERENTIATION OF PAST AND FUTURE

The last considerations seem to teach that an inference regarding past events has precisely the same nature logically as one regarding future events. In so far as, and to the extent that, causality holds at all, we may say with equal justice that the earlier determines the later and the later determines the earlier. In accordance with this all attempts to differentiate conceptually between the temporal direction from the past to the future and from future to past fail. This I believe is true also of H. Reichenbach's attempt (in the treatise cited in the *Bayrischen Sitzungsberichten*) to demonstrate the asymmetry of the causal relationship, and by its help to ascertain conceptually the positive temporal direction and thereby to be able to define even the time of the present, the now. He believes that the causal structure in the direction of the future differs topologically from that of the reverse direction. The arguments he gives for this belief I consider incorrect. However, I do not want to dwell upon this (compare for instance the critique, in need of some further elaboration, of Reichenbach's ideas by H. Bergmann in "Der Kampf um das Kausalgesetz in der jüngsten Physik") but merely to mention that the demand for a definition of the now is logically meaningless. The difference between earlier and later in physics may be described objectively, and in fact, as far as I can see, only by aid of the principle of entropy. But in this way the direction past-future is only *differentiated* from the opposite. However, that real events *proceed* in the first direction and not in the reverse cannot be said at all, and no natural law can express it. Eddington (*The Nature of the Physical World*) describes this in an intuitive way, in claiming that a positive temporal direction (time's arrow) may be defined physically, but that it is not possible to formulate conceptually the passage from the past to the future (becoming). H. Bergmann rightly sees, in opposition to H. Reichenbach, that physics has no means whatever of distinguishing the now, of defining the concept of the present. He seems, however, to assume falsely that by means of "psychological categories" this may not be impossible. In truth the meaning of the word "now" may only be *shown,* just as we may only show and not define what we understand by "blue" or by "happiness."

That the causal relation is asymmetrical, unidirectional (as Reichenbach, loc. cit. believes) is falsely suggested by facts connected with the principle of entropy. It is only due to this law that in everyday life the earlier may be more readily derived from the later than vice versa. The calculation of the later is of course not by itself identical with an inference to the future, and neither is the calculation of earlier itself identical with an inference to the past. This is the case only when the temporal point from which we make the inference is the present. Reichenbach believes (loc. cit., p. 155) that the latter case is actually distinguished by the fact that the past is objectively determined whereas the future is objectively undetermined. Brief analyses show that all that is meant by "objectively determined" is "inferable from a partial effect." The future is "objectively undetermined" because it cannot be inferred from a partial cause, for the totality of all partial causes can not be defined in the absence of determinism. All sorts of things may be said against the concepts of partial cause and partial effect, and we have already indicated that the apparently easier process of inference is falsely suggested by facts involved in the principle of entropy. But even if the argument contained no error it would again only characterise the difference between the earlier and later, not the difference between past and future.

14. INDETERMINATENESS OF NATURE AND FREEDOM OF THE WILL

The psychological reason for the sort of ideas last mentioned (and that is why I referred to them) seems to me to lie in the circumstance that, in addition to the simple meaning our analysis found for the word "undetermined," implicitly a sort of metaphysical, related meaning is attributed to it; namely, as if one could attribute determinateness or indeterminateness to a process *in itself*. That, however, is meaningless. Since "determined" means calculable by means of certain data, to speak of determinism makes sense only when we add: *By what?* Each real process whether it belongs to the past or to the future is as it is; being undetermined cannot belong to its characteristics. Regarding the natural processes themselves one cannot sensibly assert a "vagueness" of "indefiniteness." Only in reference to our thoughts may we speak of such (namely, when we do not know definitely which propositions are true, which representations are correct.) Sommerfeld evidently means just this when he says:[10] "It is not the experimentally ascertained things

10 *Scientia*, 8 (Milan, 1930) , 85.

that are indeterminate. With sufficient attention to experimental conditions, these may be precisely treated. Indeterminism applies only to our ideational forms which accompany physical facts." One must not believe therefore that modern physics has any place for the misconception of natural processes "undetermined in themselves." If, for instance, in an experiment it is not possible to give an electron a precise location, and if the same is true of its momentum, this means nothing more than that position and momentum values of a punctiform electron are not suitable means for the description of the process that takes place in nature. The modern formulations of the quantum theory recognise this and take it into account.

Just as little as the present situation in modern physics allows the formulation of a metaphysical concept of indeterminism does it allow speculations about the so-called "problem of freedom of the will" which is connected with it. This must be sharply emphasised, for not only philosophers but also men of science have not been able to withstand the temptation to utter thoughts such as the following: Science shows us that the physical universe is not fully determined; it follows, (1) that indeterminism is in the right and that physics therefore does not contradict the assertion of freedom of the will; (2) that nature, since strict causality does not prevail in it, provides room for spiritual or mental factors.

In answer to (1) we may say: the real problem regarding freedom of the will as it occurs in ethics has been confused with the question of indeterminism only because of crude errors which, since Hume, have long since been corrected. The moral freedom that the concept of responsibility presupposes does not stand in opposition to causality but would be entirely destroyed without it.[11]

To (2) we may say: the statement implies a dualism, the juxtaposition of a spiritual and physical world between which there may be an interaction because of the imperfect causality of the latter. In my opinion no philosopher has succeeded in elucidating the real *meaning* of such a proposition, that is, no one has shown which experiences would enable us to confirm its truth and which experiences would disclose its falsity. Quite the contrary, logical analysis (for which of course there is no place here) leads to the conclusion

[11] Cf. my *Fragen der Ethik* (1930), Chap. VII; English trans., *Problems of Ethics* (New York, 1939).

that in the data of experience there is no legitimate ground for that dualism. It is therefore a meaningless, untestable metaphysical proposition. It seems to be believed that the possibility of "psychical" factors entering through possible loopholes of "physical" causality has consequences relating to our world outlook that satisfy certain emotional needs. However this is an illusion (since the purely theoretical interpretation of the world has no relationship to emotional needs correctly understood). If the tiny gaps in causality could in some way be filled in, it would only mean that the above mentioned, practically insignificant traces of indeterminism existent in the modern world-picture would again be partly wiped out.

In this realm the metaphysics of earlier times was guilty of certain errors which sometimes occur even now where metaphysical motives are completely absent. Thus we read in Reichenbach (p. 141) : "If determinism is correct nothing can justify our undertaking an action for tomorrow but not for yesterday. It is clear that we then have no *possibility* at all even to abstain from the *plan* for the morrow's action and from the *belief* in freedom—certainly not, but in that case our action does not make *sense.*" It seems to me that the exact opposite is the case: our actions and plans obviously make sense *only* in so far as the future is determined by them. Here there is simply a confusion of determinism with fatalism, which has so often been criticised in the literature that we need not dwell upon it. Moreover, he who still represents the opinion criticised above would not be helped at all by the indeterminism of modern physics. For with utmost consideration of all relevant facts, happenings are still so precisely calculable beforehand in it, the remaining indeterminateness is so slight, that the significance our actions would have in this world of ours would still be vanishingly small.

Precisely the last considerations teach us again how different the contributions of modern physics to the question of causality are from those of earlier philosophical thinking; and how correct we were in saying at the very beginning that human imagination was in no position to foresee the structure of the world as revealed to us by patient investigation. For it is even difficult for it to progress in the steps science has already shown to be possible.

6

Can Quantum-Mechanical Description

of Physical Reality

Be Considered Complete?

EDITORIAL NOTE: *The two short essays that follow are the most technical ones to be included in the present collection. However, their interest for us here lies less in their technicalities than in the intellectual methods and goals which the authors employ and presuppose. In this exchange—one might say—the epistemological opposition between the modified Kantianism of Planck, as inherited by Einstein, and the positivistic empiricism of Mach, as developed by Bohr, expresses itself through the formulation of rival theoretical interpretations of certain crucial, though imaginary, examples: that is, through alternative descriptions of a Gedankenexperiment.*

The effect of this opposition is to make quite explicit, in a practical case, the new restrictions on the ambitions of theoretical physics analyzed philosophically by Schlick in the previous essay. Einstein and his colleagues are unwilling to accept as "complete" any account of a physical system which satisfies all the limitations demanded by quantum mechanics, since in their view such an account will leave out certain quite authentic elements in "physical reality." Bohr, in response, argues that the effect of quantum mechanics is to compel "a radical revision of our attitude as regards physical reality" of a sort comparable to that which Einstein himself had initiated with his relativity theory. The outcome of the exchange was of course, entirely inconclusive; but it serves admirably to show how, at this critical point in the history of physics, theoretical and epistemological issues were inextricably interrelated.

(A) A. EINSTEIN, B. PODOLSKY AND
N. ROSEN

In a complete theory there is an element coresponding to each element of reality. A sufficient condition for the reality of a physical quantity is the possibility of predicting it with certainty, without disturbing the system. In quantum mechanics in the case of two physical quantities described by non-commuting operators, the knowledge of one precludes the knowledge of the other. Then either (1) the description of reality given by the wave function in quantum mechanics is not complete or (2) these two quantities cannot have simultaneous reality. Consideration of the problem of making predictions concerning a system on the basis of measurements made on another system that had previously interacted with it leads to the result that if (1) is false then (2) is also false. One is thus led to conclude that the description of reality as given by a wave function is not complete.

I

ANY SERIOUS consideration of a physical theory must take into account the distinction between the objective reality, which is independent of any theory, and the physical concepts with which the theory operates. These concepts are intended to correspond with the objective reality, and by means of these concepts we picture this reality to ourselves.

In attempting to judge the success of a physical theory, we may ask ourselves two questions: (1) "Is the theory correct?" and (2) "Is the description given by the theory complete?" It is only in the case in which positive answers may be given to both of these questions, that the concepts of the theory may be said to be satisfactory. The correctness of the theory is judged by the degree of agreement between the conclusions of the theory and human experience. This experience, which alone enables us to make inferences about reality, in physics takes the form of experiment and measurement. It is the second question that we wish to consider here, as applied to quantum mechanics.

Whatever the meaning assigned to the term *complete,* the following requirement for a complete theory seems to be a necessary one: *every element of the physical reality must have a counterpart in the physical theory.* We shall call this the condition of completeness. The second question is thus easily answered, as soon as we are able to decide what are the elements of the physical reality.

The elements of the physical reality cannot be determined by *a priori* philosophical considerations, but must be found by an appeal to results of experiments and measurements. A comprehensive definition of reality is, however, unnecessary for our purpose. We shall be satisfied with the following criterion, which we regard as reasonable. *If, without in any way disturbing a system, we can predict with certainty (i.e., with probability equal to unity) the value of a physical quantity, then there exists an element of physical reality corresponding to this physical quantity.* It seems to us that this criterion, while far from exhausting all possible ways of recognizing a physical reality, at least provides us with one such way, whenever the conditions set down in it occur. Regarded not as a necessary, but merely as a sufficient, condition of reality, this criterion is in agreement with classical as well as quantum-mechanical ideas of reality.

To illustrate the ideas involved let us consider the quantum-mechanical description of the behavior of a particle having a single degree of freedom. The fundamental concept of the theory is the concept of *state,* which is supposed to be completely characterized by the wave function ψ, which is a function of the variables chosen to describe the particle's behavior. Corresponding to each physically observable quantity A there is an operator, which may be designated by the same letter.

If ψ is an eigenfunction of the operator A, that is, if

$$\psi' \equiv A\psi = a\psi, \qquad (1)$$

where a is a number, then the physical quantity A has with certainty the value a whenever the particle is in the state given by ψ. In accordance with our criterion of reality, for a particle in the state given by ψ for which Eq. (1) holds, there is an element of physical reality corresponding to the physical quantity A. Let, for example,

$$\psi = e^{(2\pi i/h)p_0 x}, \qquad (2)$$

where h is Planck's constant, p_0 is some constant number, and x the independent variable. Since the operator corresponding to the momentum of the particle is

$$p = (h/2\pi i)\, \partial/\partial x, \tag{3}$$

we obtain

$$\psi' = p\psi = (h/2\pi i)\, \partial\psi/\partial x = p_0\psi. \tag{4}$$

Thus, in the state given by Eq. (2), the momentum has certainly the value p_0. It thus has meaning to say that the momentum of the particle in the state given by Eq. (2) is real.

On the other hand if Eq. (1) does not hold, we can no longer speak of the physical quantity A having a particular value. This is the case, for example, with the coordinate of the particle. The operator corresponding to it, say q, is the operator of multiplication by the independent variable. Thus,

$$q\psi = x\psi \neq a\psi. \tag{5}$$

In accordance with quantum mechanics we can only say that the relative probability that a measurement of the coordinate will give a result lying between a and b is

$$P(a, b) = \int_a^b \bar{\psi}\psi\, dx = \int_a^b dx = b - a.$$

Since this probability is independent of a, but depends only upon the difference $b - a$, we see that all values of the coordinate are equally probable.

A definite value of the coordinate, for a particle in the state given by Eq. (2), is thus not predictable, but may be obtained only by a direct measurement. Such a measurement however disturbs the particle and thus alters its state. After the coordinate is determined, the particle will no longer be in the state given by Eq. (2). The usual conclusion from this in quantum mechanics is that *when the momentum of a particle is known, its coordinate has no physical reality.*

More generally, it is shown in quantum mechanics that, if the operators corresponding to two physical quantities, say A and B, do not commute, that is, if $AB \neq BA$, then the precise knowledge of one of them precludes such a knowledge of the other. Furthermore, any attempt to determine the latter experimentally will alter the state of the system in such a way as to destroy the knowledge of the first.

From this follows that either (1) *the quantum-mechanical description of reality given by the wave function is not complete* or (2) *when the operators corresponding to two physical quantities do not commute the two quantities cannot have simultaneous reality.* For if both of them had simultaneous reality—and thus definite values—these values would enter into the complete description, according to the condition of completeness. If then the wave function provided such a complete description of reality, it would contain these values; these would then be predictable. This not being the case, we are left with the alternatives stated.

In quantum mechanics it is usually assumed that the wave function *does* contain a complete description of the physical reality of the system in the state to which it corresponds. At first sight this assumption is entirely reasonable, for the information obtainable from a wave function seems to correspond exactly to what can be measured without altering the state of the system. We shall show, however, that this assumption, together with the criterion of reality given above, leads to a contradiction.

II

For this purpose let us suppose that we have two systems, I and II, which we permit to interact from the time $t = 0$ to $t = T$, after which time we suppose that there is no longer any interaction between the two parts. We suppose further that the states of the two systems before $t = 0$ were known. We can then calculate with the help of Schrödinger's equation the state of the combined system I + II at any subsequent time; in particular, for any $t > T$. Let us designate the corresponding wave function by ψ. We cannot, however, calculate the state in which either one of the two systems is left after the interaction. This, according to quantum mechanics, can be done only with the help of further measurements, by a process known as the *reduction of the wave packet.* Let us consider the essentials of this process.

Let a_1, a_2, a_3, . . . be the eigenvalues of some physical quantity A

pertaining to system I and $u_1(x_1)$, $u_2(x_1)$, $u_3(x_1)$, . . . the corresponding eigenfunctions, where x_1 stands for the variables used to describe the first system. Then ψ, considered as a function of x_1, can be expressed as

$$\psi(x_1, x_2) = \sum_{n=1}^{\infty} \psi_n(x_2)\, u_n(x_1), \tag{7}$$

where x_2 stands for the variables used to describe the second system. Here $\psi_n(x_2)$ are to be regarded merely as the coefficients of the expansion of ψ into a series of orthogonal functions $u_n(x_1)$. Suppose now that the quantity A is measured and it is found that it has the value a_k. It is then concluded that after the measurement the first system is left in the state given by the wave function $u_k(x_1)$, and that the second system is left in the state given by the wave function $\psi_k(x_2)$. This is the process of reduction of the wave packet; the wave packet given by the infinite series (7) is reduced to a single term $\psi_k(x_2)\, u_k(x_1)$.

The set of functions $u_n(x_1)$ is determined by the choice of the physical quantity A. If, instead of this, we had chosen another quantity, say B, having the eigenvalues b_1, b_2, b_3, . . . and eigenfunctions $v_1(x_1)$, $v_2(x_1)$, $v_3(x_1)$, . . . we should have obtained, instead of Eq. (7), the expansion

$$\psi(x_1, x_2) = \sum_{s=1}^{\infty} \varphi_s(x_2)\, v_s(x_1), \tag{8}$$

where φ_s's are the new coefficients. If now the quantity B is measured and is found to have the value b_r, we conclude that after the measurement the first system is left in the state given by $v_r(x_1)$ and the second system is left in the state given by $\varphi_r(x_2)$.

We see therefore that, as a consequence of two different measurements performed upon the first system, the second system may be left in states with two different wave functions. On the other hand, since at the time of measurement the two systems no longer interact, no real change can take place in the second system in consequence of anything that may be done to the first system. This is, of course, merely a statement of what is meant by the absence of an interaction between the two systems. Thus, *it is possible to assign two different wave functions* (in our example ψ_k and φ_r) *to the same reality* (the second system after the interaction with the first).

Now, it may happen that the two wave functions, ψ_k and φ_r, are eigenfunctions of two noncommuting operators corresponding to some physical quantities P and Q, respectively. That this may actually be the case can best be shown by an example. Let us suppose that the two systems are two particles, and that

$$\psi(x_1, x_2) = \int_{-\infty}^{\infty} e^{(2\pi i/h)\ (x_1 - x_2 + x_0)p} dp, \tag{9}$$

where x^0 is some constant: Let A be the momentum of the first particle; then, as we have seen in Eq. (4), its eigenfunctions will be

$$u_p(x_1) = e^{(2\pi i/h) p x_1} \tag{10}$$

corresponding to the eigenvalue p. Since we have here the case of a continuous spectrum, Eq. (7) will now be written

$$\psi(x_1, x_2) = \int_{-\infty}^{\infty} \psi_p(x_2)\, u_p(x_1)\, dp, \tag{11}$$

where

$$\psi_p(x_2) = e^{-(2\pi i/h)\ (x_2 - x_0)\ p}. \tag{12}$$

This ψ_p however is the eigenfunction of the operator

$$P = (h/2\pi i)\, \partial/\partial x_2, \tag{13}$$

corresponding to the eigenvalue $-p$ of the momentum of the second particle. On the other hand, if B is the coordinate of the first particle, it has for eigenfunctions

$$v_x(x_1) = \delta(x_1 - x), \tag{14}$$

corresponding to the eigenvalue x, where $\delta(x_1 - x)$ is the well-known Dirac delta-function. Eq. (8) in this case becomes

$$\psi(x_1, x_2) = \int_{-\infty}^{\infty} \varphi_x(x_2)\, v_x(x_1)\, dx, \tag{15}$$

where

$$\varphi_x(x_2) = \int e^{(2\pi i/h)\,(x-x_2+x_0)p} dp$$

$$= h\delta(x - x_2 + x_0). \tag{16}$$

This φ_x, however, is the eigenfunction of the operator

$$Q = x_2 \tag{17}$$

corresponding to the eigenvalue $x + x_0$ of the coordinate of the second particle. Since

$$PQ - QP = h/2\pi i, \tag{18}$$

we have shown that it is in general possible for ψ_k and φ_r to be eigenfunctions of two noncommuting operators, corresponding to physical quantities.

Returning now to the general case contemplated in Eqs. (7) and (8), we assume that ψ_k and φ_r are indeed eigenfunctions of some noncommuting operators P and Q, corresponding to the eigenvalues p_k and q_r, respectively. Thus, by measuring either A or B we are in a position to predict with certainty, and without in any way disturbing the second system, either the value of the quantity P (that is p_k) or the value of the quantity Q (that is q_r). In accordance with our criterion of reality, in the first case we must consider the quantity P as being an element of reality, in the second case the quantity Q is an element of reality. But, as we have seen, both wave functions ψ_k and φ_r belong to the same reality.

Previously we proved that either (1) the quantum-mechanical description of reality given by the wave function is not complete or (2) when the operators corresponding to two physical quantities do not commute the two quantities cannot have simultaneous reality. Starting then with the assumption that the wave function does give a complete description of the physical reality, we arrived at the conclusion that two physical quantities, with noncommuting operators, can have simultaneous reality. Thus the negation of (1) leads to the negation of the only other alternative (2). We are thus forced to conclude that the quantum-mechanical description of physical reality given by wave functions is not complete.

One could object to this conclusion on the grounds that our criterion of reality is not sufficiently restrictive. Indeed, one would not arrive at our conclusion if one insisted that two or more physical quantities can be regarded as simultaneous elements of reality *only when they can be simultaneously measured or predicted*. On this point of view, since either one or the other, but not both simultaneously, of the quantities P and Q can be predicted, they are not simultaneously real. This makes the reality of P and Q depend upon the process of measurement carried out on the first system, which does not disturb the second system in any way. No reasonable definition of reality could be expected to permit this.

While we have thus shown that the wave function does not provide a complete description of the physical reality, we left open the question of whether or not such a description exists. We believe, however, that such a theory is possible.

(B) N. BOHR

IT IS shown that a certain "criterion of physical reality" formulated in a recent article with the above title by A. Einstein, B. Podolsky and N. Rosen contains an essential ambiguity when it is applied to quantum phenomena. In this connection a viewpoint termed "complementarity" is explained from which quantum-mechanical description of physical phenomena would seem to fulfill, within its scope, all rational demands of completeness.

In a recent article[1] under the above title A. Einstein, B. Podolsky and N. Rosen have presented arguments which lead them to answer the question at issue in the negative. The trend of their argumentation, however, does not seem to me adequately to meet the actual situation with which we are faced in atomic physics. I shall therefore be glad to use this opportunity to explain in somewhat greater detail a general viewpoint, conveniently termed "complementarity," which I have indicated on various previous occasions,[2] and

[1] A. Einstein, B. Podolsky and N. Rosen, *Phys. Rev.,* (1935) , 47.
[2] Cf. Niels Bohr, *Atomic Theory and Description of Nature,* I (Cambridge, 1934) .

from which quantum mechanics within its scope would appear as a completely rational description of physical phenomena, such as we meet in atomic processes.

The extent to which an unambiguous meaning can be attributed to such an expression as "physical reality" cannot of course be deduced from *a priori* philosophical conceptions, but—as the authors of the article cited themselves emphasize—must be founded on a direct appeal to experiments and measurements. For this purpose they propose a "criterion of reality" formulated as follows: "If, without in any way disturbing a system, we can predict with certainty the value of a physical quantity, then there exists an element of physical reality corresponding to this physical quantity." By means of an interesting example, to which we shall return below, they next proceed to show that in quantum mechanics, just as in classical mechanics, it is possible under suitable conditions to predict the value of any given variable pertaining to the description of a mechanical system from measurements performed entirely on other systems which previously have been in interaction with the system under investigation. According to their criterion the authors therefore want to ascribe an element of reality to each of the quantities represented by such variables. Since, moreover, it is a well-known feature of the present formalism of quantum mechanics that it is never possible, in the description of the state of a mechanical system, to attach definite values to both of two canonically conjugate variables, they consequently deem this formalism to be incomplete, and express the belief that a more satisfactory theory can be developed.

Such an argumentation, however, would hardly seem suited to affect the soundness of quantum-mechanical description, which is based on a coherent mathematical formalism covering automatically any procedure of measurement like that indicated.[3] The ap-

---

[3] The deductions contained in the article cited may in this respect be considered as an immediate consequence of the transformation theorems of quantum mechanics, which perhaps more than any other feature of the formalism contribute to secure its mathematical completeness and its rational correspondence with classical mechanics. In fact, it is always possible in the description of a mechanical system, consisting of two partial systems (1) and (2), interacting or not, to replace any two pairs of canonically conjugate variables $(q_1 p_1)$, $(q_2 p_2)$ pertain-

parent contradiction in it discloses only an essential inadequacy of the customary viewpoint of natural philosophy for a causal account of physical phenomena of the sort with which we are concerned in quantum mechanics. Indeed the *finite interaction between object and measuring agencies* conditioned by the very existence of the quantum of action entails—because of the impossibility of controlling the action of the object on the measuring instruments if these are to serve their purpose—the necessity of a final renunciation of the classical ideal of causality and a radical revision of our attitude towards the problem of physical reality. In fact, as we shall see, a criterion of reality like that proposed by the named authors contains—however cautious its formulation may appear—an essential ambiguity when it is applied to the actual problems with which we are here concerned. In order to make the argument to this end as clear as possible, I shall first consider in some detail a few simple examples of measuring arrangements.

Let us begin with the simple case of a particle passing through a slit in a diaphragm, which may form part of some more or less complicated experimental arrangement. Even if the momentum of

---

ing to systems (1) and (2), respectively, and satisfying the usual commutation rules

$$[q_1 p_1] = [q_2 p_2] = ih/2\pi,$$
$$[q_1 q_2] = [p_1 p_2] = q_1 p_2 [q_2 p_1] = 0,$$

by two pairs of new conjugate variables $(Q_1 P_1)$, $(Q_2 P_2)$ related to the first variables by a simple orthogonal transformation, corresponding to a rotation of angle θ in the planes $(q_1 q_2)$, $(p_1 p_2)$

$$q_1 = Q_1 \cos \theta - Q_2 \sin \theta \qquad\qquad p_1 = P_1 \cos \theta - P_2 \sin \theta$$
$$q_2 = Q_1 \sin \theta + Q_2 \cos \theta \qquad\qquad p_2 = P_1 \sin \theta + P_2 \cos \theta.$$

Since these variables will satisfy analogous commutation rules, in particular

$$[Q_1 P_1] = ih/2\pi, \qquad [Q_1 P_2] = 0,$$

it follows that in the description of the state of the combined system definite numerical values may not be assigned to both Q_1 and P_1, but that we may clearly assign such values to both Q_1 and P_2. In that case it further results from the expressions of these variables in terms of $(q_1 p_1)$ and $(q_2 p_2)$, namely

$$Q_1 = q_1 \cos \theta + q_2 \sin \theta, \qquad P_2 = -p_1 \sin \theta + p_2 \cos \theta,$$

that a subsequent measurement of either q_2 or p_2 will allow us to predict the value of q_1 or p_1 respectively.

this particle is completely known before it impinges on the diaphragm, the diffraction by the slit of the plane wave giving the symbolic representation of its state will imply an uncertainty in the momentum of the particle, after it has passed the diaphragm, which is the greater the narrower the slit. Now the width of the slit, at any rate if it is still large compared with the wave-length, may be taken as the uncertainty Δq of the position of the particle relative to the diaphragm, in a direction perpendicular to the slit. Moreover, it is simply seen from de Broglie's relation between momentum and wave-length that the uncertainty Δp of the momentum of the particle in this direction is correlated to Δq by mean of Heisenberg's general principle

$$\Delta p \Delta q \sim h,$$

which in the quantum-mechanical formalism is a direct consequence of the commutation relation for any pair of conjugate variables. Obviously the uncertainty Δp is inseparably connected with the possibility of an exchange of momentum between the particle and the diaphragm; and the question of principal interest for our discussion is now to what extent the momentum thus exchanged can be taken into account in the description of the phenomenon to be studied by the experimental arrangement concerned, of which the passing of the particle through the slit may be considered as the initial stage.

Let us first assume that, corresponding to usual experiments on the remarkable phenomena of electron diffraction, the diaphragm, like the other parts of the apparatus,—say a second diaphragm with several slits parallel to the first and a photographic plate,—is rigidly fixed to a support which defines the space frame of reference. Then the momentum exchanged between the particle and the diaphragm will, together with the reaction of the particle on the other bodies, pass into this common support, and we have thus voluntarily cut ourselves off from any possibility of taking these reactions separately into account in predictions regarding the final result of the experiment,—say the position of the spot produced by the particle on the photographic plate. The impossibility of a closer analysis of the reactions between the particle and the measuring instrument is indeed no peculiarity of the experimental procedure described, but is rather an essential property of any arrangement suited to the study of the phenomena of the type concerned, where we have to do with a feature of *individuality* completely foreign to classical physics. In fact, any possibility of taking into account the momentum exchanged between the particle and the separate parts of the apparatus would at once permit us to draw conclusions regarding the "course" of such phenomena,—say through what particular slit of the second diaphragm the particle passes on its way to the photographic plate—which would be quite incompatible with the fact that the probability of the particle reaching a given element of area on this plate is determined not by the presence of any particular slit, but by the positions of all the slits of the second diaphragm within reach of the associated wave diffracted from the slit of the first diaphragm.

By another experimental arrangement, where the first diaphragm is not rigidly connected with the other parts of the apparatus, it would at least in principle[4] be possible to measure its momentum with any desired accuracy before and after the passage of the particle, and thus to predict the momentum of the latter after it has passed through the slit. In fact, such measurements of momentum require only an unambiguous application of the classical law of conservation of momentum, applied for instance to a collision process between the diaphragm and some test body, the momentum of which is suitably controlled before and after the collision. It is true that such a control will essentially depend on an examination of the space-time course of some process to which the ideas of classical mechanics can be applied; if, however, all spatial dimensions and time intervals are taken sufficiently large, this involves clearly no limitation as regards the accurate control of the momentum of the test bodies, but only a renunciation as regards the accuracy of the control of their space-time coordination. This last circumstance is in fact quite analogous to the renunciation of the control of the momentum of the fixed diaphragm in the experi-

---

[4] The obvious impossibility of actually carrying out, with the experimental technique at our disposal, such measuring procedures as are discussed here and in the following does clearly not affect the theoretical argument, since the procedures in question are essentially equivalent with atomic processes, like the Compton effect, where a corresponding application of the conservation theorem of momentum is well established.

mental arrangement discussed above, and depends in the last resort on the claim of a purely classical account of the measuring apparatus, which implies the necessity of allowing a latitude corresponding to the quantum-mechanical uncertainty relations in our description of their behavior.

The principal difference between the two experimental arrangements under consideration is, however, that in the arrangement suited for the control of the momentum of the first diaphragm, this body can no longer be used as a measuring instrument for the same purpose as in the previous case, but must, as regards its position relative to the rest of the apparatus, be treated, like the particle traversing the slit, as an object of investigation, in the sense that the quantum-mechanical uncertainty relations regarding its position and momentum must be taken explicitly into account. In fact, even if we knew the position of the diaphragm relative to the space frame before the first measurement of its momentum, and even though its position after the last measurement can be accurately fixed, we lose, on account of the uncontrollable displacement of the diaphragm during each collision process with the test bodies, the knowledge of its position when the particle passed through the slit. The whole arrangement is therefore obviously unsuited to study the same kind of phenomena as in the previous case. In particular it may be shown that, if the momentum of the diaphragm is measured with an accuracy sufficient for allowing definite conclusions regarding the passage of the particle through some selected slit of the second diaphragm, then even the minimum uncertainty of the position of the first diaphragm compatible with such a knowledge will imply the total wiping out of any interference effect—regarding the zones of permitted impact of the particle on the photographic plate—to which the presence of more than one slit in the second diaphragm would give rise in case the positions of all apparatus are fixed relative to each other.

In an arrangement suited for measurements of the momentum of the first diaphragm, it is further clear that even if we have measured this momentum before the passage of the particle through the slit, we are after this passage still left with a *free choice* whether we wish to know the momentum of the particle or its initial position relative to the rest of the apparatus. In the first eventuality we need only to make a second determination of the momentum of the diaphragm, leaving unknown forever its exact position when the particle passed. In the second eventuality we need only to determine its position relative to the space frame with the inevitable loss of the knowledge of the momentum exchanged between the diaphragm and the particle. If the diaphragm is sufficiently massive in comparison with the particle, we may even arrange the procedure of measurements in such a way that the diaphragm after the first determination of its momentum will remain at rest in some unknown position relative to the other parts of the apparatus, and the subsequent fixation of this position may therefore simply consist in establishing a rigid connection between the diaphragm and the common support.

My main purpose in repeating these simple, and in substance well-known considerations, is to emphasize that in the phenomena concerned we are not dealing with an incomplete description characterized by the arbitrary picking out of different elements of physical reality at the cost of sacrificing other such elements, but with a rational discrimination between essentially different experimental arrangements and procedures which are suited either for an unambiguous use of the idea of space location, or for a legitimate application of the conservation theorem of momentum. Any remaining appearance of arbitrariness concerns merely our freedom of handling the measuring instruments, characteristic of the very idea of experiment. In fact, the renunciation in each experimental arrangement of the one or the other of two aspects of the description of physical phenomena,—the combination of which characterizes the method of classical physics, and which therefore in this sense may be considered as *complementary* to one another,—depends essentially on the impossibility, in the field of quantum theory, of accurately controlling the reaction of the object on the measuring instruments, i.e., the transfer of momentum in case of position measurements, and the displacement in case of momentum measurements. Just in this last respect any comparison between quantum mechanics and ordinary statistical mechanics,—however useful it may be for the formal presentation of the theory,—is essentially irrelevant. Indeed we have in each experimental arrangement suited for the study of proper quantum phenomena not merely to do with an ignorance of the value of certain physical quantities, but with the impossibility of defining these quantitites in an unambiguous way.

The last remarks apply equally well to the special problem treated by Einstein, Podolsky and Rosen, which has been referred to above, and which does not actually involve any greater intricacies than the simple examples discussed above. The particular quantum-mechanical state of two free particles, for which they give an explicit mathematical expression, may be reproduced, at least in principle, by a simple experimental arrangement, comprising a rigid diaphragm with two parallel slits, which are very narrow compared with their separation, and through each of which one particle with given initial momentum passes independently of the other. If the momentum of this diaphragm is measured accurately before as well as after the passing of the particles, we shall in fact know the sum of the components perpendicular to the slits of the momenta of the two escaping particles, as well as the difference of their initial positional coordinates in the same direction; while of course the conjugate quantities, i.e., the difference of the components of their momenta, and the sum of their positional coordinates, are entirely unknown.[5] In this arrangement, it is therefore clear that a subsequent single measurement either of the position or of the momentum of one of the particles will automatically determine the position or momentum, respectively, of the other particle with any desired accuracy; at least if the wave-length corresponding to the free motion of each particle is sufficiently short compared with the width of the slits. As pointed out by the named authors, we are therefore faced at this stage with a completely free choice whether we want to determine the one or the other of the latter quantities by a process which does not directly interfere with the particle concerned.

Like the above simple case of the choice between the experimental procedures suited for the prediction of the position or the

---

[5] As will be seen, this description, apart from a trivial normalizing factor, corresponds exactly to the transformation of variables described in the preceding footnote if $(q_1 p_1)$, $(q_2 p_2)$ represent the positional coordinates and components of momenta of the two particles and if $\theta = -\pi/4$. It may also be remarked that the wave function given by formula (9) of the article cited corresponds to the special choice of $P_2 = 0$ and the limiting case of two infinitely narrow slits.

momentum of a single particle which has passed through a slit in a diaphragm, we are, in the "freedom of choice" offered by the last arrangement, just concerned with a *discrimination between different experimental procedures which allow of the unambiguous use of complementary classical concepts.* In fact to measure the position of one of the particles can mean nothing else than to establish a correlation between its behavior and some instrument rigidly fixed to the support which defines the space frame of reference. Under the experimental conditions described such a measurement will therefore also provide us with the knowledge of the location, otherwise completely unknown, of the diaphragm with respect to this space frame when the particles passed through the slits. Indeed, only in this way we obtain a basis for conclusions about the initial position of the other particle relative to the rest of the apparatus. By allowing an essentially uncontrollable momentum to pass from the first particle into the mentioned support, however, we have by this procedure cut ourselves off from any future possibility of applying the law of conservation of momentum to the system consisting of the diaphragm and the two particles and therefore have lost our only basis for an unambiguous application of the idea of momentum in predictions regarding the behavior of the second particle. Conversely, if we choose to measure the momentum of one of the particles, we lose through the uncontrollable displacement inevitable in such a measurement any possibility of deducing from the behavior of this particle the position of the diaphragm relative to the rest of the apparatus, and have thus no basis whatever for predictions regarding the location of the other particle.

From our point of view we now see that the wording of the above-mentioned criterion of physical reality proposed by Einstein, Podolsky and Rosen contains an ambiguity as regards the meaning of the expression "without in any way disturbing a system." Of course there is in a case like that just considered no question of a mechanical disturbance of the system under investigation during the last critical stage of the measuring procedure. But even at this stage there is essentially the question of *an influence on the very conditions which define the possible types of predictions regarding the future behavior of the system.* Since these conditions constitute an inherent element of the description of any phenomenon to which the term "physical reality" can be properly attached, we see that the argumentation of the mentioned authors does not justify their conclusion that quantum-mechanical description is essentially incomplete. On the contrary this description, as appears from the preceding discussion, may be characterized as a rational utilization of all possibilities of unambiguous interpretation of measurements, compatible with the finite and uncontrollable interaction between the objects and the measuring instruments in the field of quantum theory. In fact, it is only the mutual exclusion of any two experimental procedures, permitting the unambiguous definition of complementary physical quantities, which provides room for new physical laws, the coexistence of which might at first sight appear irreconcilable with the basic principles of science. It is just this entirely new situation as regards the description of physical phenomena, that the notion of *complementarity* aims at characterizing.

The experimental arrangements hitherto discussed present a special simplicity on account of the secondary role which the idea of time plays in the description of the phenomena in question. It is true that we have freely made use of such words as "before" and "after" implying time-relationships; but in each case allowance must be made for a certain inaccuracy, which is of no importance, however, so long as the time intervals concerned are sufficiently large compared with the proper periods entering in the closer analysis of the phenomenon under investigation. As soon as we attempt a more accurate time description of quantum phenomena, we meet with well-known new paradoxes, for the elucidation of which further features of the interaction between the objects and the measuring instruments must be taken into account. In fact, in such phenomena we have no longer to do with experimental arrangements consisting of apparatus essentially at rest relative to one another, but with arrangements containing moving parts,—like shutters before the slits of the diaphragms,—controlled by mechanisms serving as clocks. Besides the transfer of momentum, discussed above, between the object and the bodies defining the space frame, we shall therefore, in such arrangements, have to consider an eventual exchange of energy between the object and these clock-like mechanisms.

The decisive point as regards time measurements in quantum

theory is now completely analogous to the argument concerning measurements of positions outlined above. Just as the transfer of momentum to the separate parts of the apparatus,—the knowledge of the relative positions of which is required for the description of the phenomenon,—has been seen to be entirely uncontrollable, so the exchange of energy between the object and the various bodies, whose relative motion must be known for the intended use of the apparatus, will defy any closer analysis. Indeed, it is *excluded in principle to control the energy which goes into the clocks without interfering essentially with their use as time indicators.* This use in fact entirely relies on the assumed possibility of accounting for the functioning of each clock as well as for its eventual comparison with other clocks on the basis of the methods of classical physics. In this account we must therefore obviously allow for a latitude in the energy balance, corresponding to the quantum-mechanical uncertainty relation for the conjugate time and energy variables. Just as in the question discussed above of the mutually exclusive character of any unambiguous use in quantum theory of the concepts of position and momentum, it is in the last resort this circumstance which entails the complementary relationship between any detailed time account of atomic phenomena on the one hand and the unclassical features of intrinsic stability of atoms, disclosed by the study of energy transfers in atomic reactions on the other hand.

This necessity of discriminating in each experimental arrangement between those parts of the physical system considered which are to be treated as measuring instruments and those which constitute the objects under investigation may indeed be said to form a *principal distinction between classical and quantum-mechanical description of physical phenomena.* It is true that the place within each measuring procedure where this discrimination is made is in both cases largely a matter of convenience. While, however, in classical physics the distinction between object and measuring agencies does not entail any difference in the character of the description of the phenomena concerned, its fundamental importance in quantum theory, as we have seen, has its root in the indispensable use of classical concepts in the interpretation of all proper measurements, even though the classical theories do not suffice in accounting for the new types of regularities with which we are concerned in atomic physics. In accordance with this situation there can be no question of any unambiguous interpretation of the symbols of quantum mechanics other than that embodied in the well-known rules which allow to predict the results to be obtained by a given experimental arrangement described in a totally classical way, and which have found their general expression through the transformation theorems, already referred to. By securing its proper correspondence with the classical theory, these theorems exclude in particular any imaginable inconsistency in the quantum-mechanical description, connected with a change of the place where the discrimination is made between object and measuring agencies. In fact it is an obvious consequence of the above argumentation that in each experimental arrangement and measuring procedure we have only a free choice of this place within a region where the quantum-mechanical description of the process concerned is effectively equivalent with the classical description.

Before concluding I should still like to emphasize the bearing of the great lesson derived from general relativity theory upon the question of physical reality in the field of quantum theory. In fact, notwithstanding all characteristic differences, the situations we are concerned with in these generalizations of classical theory present striking analogies which have often been noted. Especially, the singular position of measuring instruments in the account of quantum phenomena, just discussed, appears closely analogous to the well-known necessity in relativity theory of upholding an ordinary description of all measuring processes, including a sharp distinction between space and time coordinates, although the very essence of this theory is the establishment of new physical laws, in the comprehension of which we must renounce the customary separation of space and time ideas.[6] The dependence on the reference system, in relativity theory, of all readings of scales and clocks may even be compared with the essentially uncontrollable exchange of momentum or energy between the objects of measurements and all instruments defining the space-time system of reference, which in

6 Just this circumstance, together with the relativistic invariance of the uncertainty relations of quantum mechanics, ensures the compatibility between the argumentation outlined in the present article and all exigencies of relativity theory. . . .

quantum theory confronts us with the situation characterized by the notion of complementarity. In fact this new feature of natural philosophy means a radical revision of our attitude as regards physical reality, which may be paralleled with the fundamental modification of all ideas regarding the absolute character of physical phenomena, brought about by the general theory of relativity.

7

The Copenhagen Interpretation

of Quantum Theory

by NORWOOD RUSSELL HANSON

EDITORIAL NOTE: *Professor Hanson's essay speaks for itself. True, it pleads in frankly partisan tones. Hanson is consciously putting the case for the "orthodox" interpretation of quantum mechanics, as supported by such men as Niels Bohr and Werner Heisenberg, and ridiculing the opposition view. But it is pleading of the best kind: the pleading of an advocate who believes that his client has a cast-iron case, which needs only to be set out fully and clearly enough in order to cary conviction. There are occasional rhetorical tricks— "Exit de Broglie" and the like—but otherwise the historical development and intellectual foundations of quantum mechanics are set out coolly and systematically, in the expectation of demonstrating the transparent reasonableness of Bohr's position. This has probably never been better done.*

In the course of the exposition, several important points are made clear. For instance, Hanson insists—rightly—that the transition from classical particle physics and wave theory to twentieth-century quantum mechanics had involved dovetailing two intellectual systems which, as originally formulated, were conceptually *inconsistent. The difficulty with quantum theory was not just, as has often been implied, that it was counterintuitive: rather, its procedures were, on the face of it, self-contradictory or, as Hanson puts it, "notationally impossible." The problem, then, was to find a new mode/notation/ language for describing* nature *on the sub-atomic level—to frame a new system of concepts that would escape the "notational" limitations of the classical theories and permit "a unified description of nature."*

Yet in the course of the argument, moderate as it is, the vulnerable points in the Copenhagen position are still detectable. On the one hand, Hanson does nothing to conceal the positivistic streak in the Bohr-Heisenberg interpretation or to disguise the restrictions it places on the physicist's aims. Thus, where Planck had spoken of "the physicist's way of thinking" in ambitious terms, Hanson now accepts that "in general, a physicist will use a formalism only so far as its parameters are testable," and treats the heart of any theory as lying in the mathematical algorithms it provides for deriving predictions. Again, he endorses the orthodox view that the existence of Planck's quantum of action is an argument for believing that hypothetical processes on a sub-quantum scale must inevitably remain undetectable, unknowable, and so not worth speculating about.

These concessions to positivism—which Hanson himself would have qualified on a less partisan occasion—must be borne in mind if we are to understand the full force of the subsequent argument, as illustrated by the essays of Feyerabend and Bohm. As we shall see, Feyerabend challenges directly the view that theoretical speculation in physics is to be taken seriously, only when it yields fully fledged or, in Hanson's words, "clear, detailed, physically intelligible alternative" systems of theory, capable of doing all that the current theories do, and more. On the contrary, if that requirement had been insisted on throughout, the revolt against Aristotelianism in the sixteenth and seventeenth centuries could never have got under way. As for the argument that hypothetical sub-quantum events, being "unknowable," are without physical meaning: this was the very type of argument used by Ernst Mach against the atomic theory.

Still, Bohr's position is impressive enough to be worth stating clearly and fully; and it is only against such a historical and logical background as Hanson provides that its residual weaknesses can be truly recognized for what they are.

The theoretical and experimental context within which the "Copenhagen Interpretation" of quantum theory was generated is underemphasized by recent critics of the Bohr-Heisenberg philosophy. When an interpretation of a theory has been as successful as this one has been, there is little practical warrant for the "alternative interpretations" which have, since Bohm, been receiving prominence. Indeed, these are not even genuine alternatives; although rich in provocative prose, they provide not a scrap of algebra with which to organize the practical physicist's thinking. Several objections to the Bohr interpretation are critically examined, as is also a particular use of the correspondence principle which has seemed to cast doubt on the Copenhagen ideas.

I

IT HAS become fashionable amongst philosophers of science to attack the "Copenhagen Interpretation" of quantum theory as being either unrealistic,[1] unreflective,[2] or unnecessary.[3] The present paper may be vulnerable to the same objections, but it aims to locate this "interpretation" in its historical and conceptual context, and to argue for orthodox quantum theory as it now stands. Certainly no reinterpretation yet suggested by philosopher or physicist presents a case for abandoning Bohr's view.

The Bohr theory of the Twenties issues from seeds a century old. Controversy over the nature of light was analogous to our present discussions about interpreting $|\psi(q)|^2$. Grimaldi's undulatory theory,[4] developed by Huygens,[5] speculated about by Hooke,[6] and confirmed by Young,[7] Fizeau,[8] and Foucault,[9] encountered the opposition of corpuscularians like Newton,[10] Biot,[11] Boscovich,[12] and LaPlace.[13] The plot is intricate, but it resolves in the 19th century, when the work of Young and Foucault came to be seen as decisive *against* the particulate theory.

[1] H. Mehlberg, "The Observational Problem of Quantum Theory," read at the May, 1958, meeting of the American Philosophical Association, Western Division.

[2] D. Bohm, *Phys. Rev.* 85 (1952), 166, 180.

[3] P. Feyerabend, "The Quantum Theory of Measurement," in *Observation and Interpretation* (London: Butterworth, 1957).

[4] Franciscus Maria Grimaldi, *Physico-mathesis de lumine coloribis et iride* (Bologna, 1665).

[5] Christian Huygens, *Traité de la lumière* (Leiden, 1690).

[6] Robert Hooke, *Micrographia* . . . (London, 1664).

[7] Thomas Young, *Lectures on Natural Philosophy* (London, 1807).

[8] A. H. Fizeau, *Ann. de Chim. et Phys.*, 29 (1849).

[9] J. B. Foucault, *Rec. trav. sci.* (Paris, 1878).

[10] Isaac Newton, *Philosophiae Naturalis Principia Mathematica; Opticks* (London, 1687; 1704).

[11] M. A. Biot, *Traité de physique experimentale et mathématique* (Paris, 1816).

[12] R. J. Boscovich, *Philosophiae Naturalis Theoria* (Venice, 1763).

[13] P. S. LaPlace, *Oeuvres* (Paris, 1878–1912).

Young's work, of course, proves *only* that light is wave-like,—not that it is in no way corpuscular. The latter conclusion follows only from assuming, in addition to Young's data, an exclusive use of the disjunction "light is wave-like or corpuscular (but never both at once)." Newton would not have accepted this rider. Foucault, however, needed no such logical preface. He crushed a cornerstone of Newton's *Opticks* by proving that the velocity of light decreases as the density of its medium increases. This refutes the theory of particulate attraction with which Newton [14] accounted for Snell's law.

A logical monument was built by the wave theorists to mark this defeat. Poisson, Green, MacCullagh, Neumann, Kelvin, Rayleigh, Kirchhoff, and most notably, Clerk Maxwell[15] developed the heritage of Young and Fresnel. In all their work the ideas of particle and wave came to be fashioned in logical opposition. Particle dynamics and electrodynamics matured as maturally exclusive and incompatible theories. Why? Because of (1) the apparent logic of the crucial experiment of Foucault, and (2) the conviction that either one of these two theories could explain every type of energy transfer. Yet the theories could never be applied simultaneously to the same event. A particle is an entity with ideally sharp coordinates, i.e., it is in one place at one time. No two particles can share the same place at t,—this is the logic of punctiform masses in Newton's *Principia*. They collide and rebound, with a precisely calculable energy exchange. A wave disturbance, however, essentially lacks sharp coordinates. It spreads boundlessly through the undulating medium. The expression "wave motion at a geometrical point" would be, for Maxwell and Newton both, unintelligible.[16] Moreover, two waves can be in the same place at once, as when surf waves cross at a point. Nor is there in wave motion anything strictly like particulate collision, impact, and recoil. (This follows from the wave-theoretic law of linear superposition.) So obvious was this to our great-grandfathers, and so precise its expression in the algebra

---

[14] Reference 10, Book I, Sec. XIV; Propositions XCIV–XCVIII; *Opticks*, Book I, Part I; VI.

[15] James Clerk Maxwell, *Treatise on Electricity and Magnetism* (Oxford: Clarendon Press, 1881); *Scientific Papers* (New York: Dover, 1952).

[16] Cf. reference 10, Prop. XLII, Theorem XXXIII; cf., also, *Phil. Trans. Roy. Soc.* (London), 88.

of Maxwell and Lorentz, that one could treat any class of wave properties α, β, γ, as the obverse of some comparable class of particulate properties, $\sim\alpha$, $\sim\beta$, $\sim\gamma$. It was unthinkable that an event should be at once describable both ways: this means not just *unimaginable*, but *notationally* impossible. In the only languages available for describing particle and wave dynamics such a joint description would have constituted a contradiction. Wave and particle ideas were now become conceptual opposites.

There is the kernel of the Copenhagen interpretation, because the fact is that nature refused to live up to 19th century expectations. One need only consider the discontinuous emission of energy from radiant blackbodies,[17] the discovery that photoelectron energy rises with the *frequency* of the incident light, and is independent of intensity,[18] the photon theory of Einstein,[19] the effects discovered by Compton[20] and Raman,[21] and the first confirmations of the de Broglie-Schrödinger wave theory of matter[22] by Davisson, Germer[23] and G. P. Thomas.[24] All this showed that microparticles could be described only jointly,—in particulate and wave-like terms simultaneously. Yet the only such terms available were the inflexible legacy of Maxwell's successors. From the necessity of describing nature thus arises all the conceptual constraints of quantum theory, including the Copenhagen interpretation.

In microphysics it is arbitrary whether one uses a wave or a particle language for descriptions,—just so one is aware that *both are jointly valid*. Several conclusions follow, which it is the merit of the Copenhagen school boldly to have adopted. The fact is that the microphenomenon is a conspiracy of wave and particle properties. But after admitting this (as one must) one must then also maintain a symmetry between these modes of description in all further

[17] M. Planck, *Ann. Physik*, 4 (1901), 553; *Verh. Deuts. phys.*, 2 (1900), 176.

[18] P. E. A. Lenard, *Ann. Physik*, 8 (1902), 149.

[19] Albert Einstein, *Ann. Physik*, 17 (1905), 132; R. Millikan [*Phil. Mag.*, 34 (1917)], indirectly confirms this theory.

[20] A. H. Compton, *Phys. Rev.*, 21 (1923), 483.

[21] C. V. Raman, cf. Pringsheim, *Naturw.*, 16 (1928), 597.

[22] L. de Broglie, theses (Paris, 1924); Erwin Schrödinger, *Ann. Phys.*, 79 (1926), 361.

[23] C. J. Davisson and L. H. Germer, *Nature*, 119 (1927), 558; *Phys. Rev.*, 30 (1927), 705.

[24] G. P. Thomson, *Proc. Phys. Soc.* (London) 117 (1928), 600.

theoretical work. Thus in a two-electron interaction, the description may run: electron creates field; field acts on another electron. But we can always find a parallel particulate description: electron emits photon; photon is absorbed by another electron. Consider also proton-neutron interaction. In wave notation: neutron creates field; field acts on proton. But we will often say: neutron emits electron plus neutrino; electron and neutrino are absorbed by proton.[25]

This resolution not to sacrifice either notation, the facts being what they are, leads to a qualitative appreciation of the uncertainty relations. This is how it came to Heisenberg.[26] Because if the micro-phenomenon—an orbiting electron—is provisionally described as a cluster of the interferences maxima of an otherwise undefined wave group, then precisely to locate it (as a "punctiform mass") at the intersection of four coordinates would require introducing an infinite number of further waves (of infinitely varying amplitudes and frequencies) so as to increase destructive interference along the line of propagation and "squeeze" the packet to a "vertical" line (in configuration space, of course). This renders unknowable the particle's energy, which is intimately associated with the amplitude and frequency of the component phase waves. But if we would determine the particle's energy, then the phase waves must be decreased in number, allowing the "wavicle" to spread "monochromatically" through the whole configuration space. Thus $\psi(\mathrm{x},0) = (\frac{1}{2}\pi\hbar)^{3/2}\iiint_p a(p)\,e^{(i/\hbar)\mathrm{p}\cdot\mathrm{x}}dp$. That is, the more narrow $\psi(x,0)$ is chosen, the broader the bracket of linear momenta p—the quicker the component plane waves get out of phase, and the "peaked" packet disintegrates. So also, the square of $\psi(p)$ represents the probability of finding our particles with certain momenta if we carry out an experiment measuring linear momenta. This interpretation shows qualitatively the impossibility of determining with precision at t all the 2^n canonical coordinates of a quantum-mechanical system.

Thus when micronature forced a wedding between the concepts classical physics had sundered, three disconcerting notions emerged as issue of the marriage: 1. Physicists were obliged not to overstress either phase of the new joint notation unless nature dictated this

25 Cf. W. Heisenberg, *Nuclear Physics* (London, 1953), p. 98.
26 W. Heisenberg, *Z. Physik,* 41 (1927), 239.

(present experience provides no basis for expecting such a dictation). 2. They became aware of a deep conceptual limitation—the uncertainty relations. 3. They saw the need of a single formalism which could integrate these inharmonious ideas, "wave" and "particle," into one algorithm.

Of the "old" quantum theories of 1913[27] and 1916[28] I shall remark only that they were classical models of the "Saturnian" atom proposed by Nagaoka[29] and Rutherford,[30] into which was forced (without reasons) the idea of quantizing electronic orbits. Then de Broglie simply hammered together the wave and particle notations.[31] He had no clear notion of a physical interpretation of these waves, and perhaps still has not. Schrödinger then took de Broglie's *ondes de phase* literally as classical fields of the Maxwell type.[32] This interpretation was punctured by Born[33] as we shall see in the following. So the elegant wave mechanics of Schrödinger, and the observationally equivalent matrix mechanics of Heisenberg,[34] had to float for a time in a cloud of uncertainty concerning just what experimental sense there is in several parameters connected with $|\psi(q)|^2$. Born dispelled this cloud with the ingenious suggestion that the waves be taken as a measure of the probability of locating particles within a given volume element.[35] Because it was operationally clear, and corroborated by every known experiment, Born's view was quickly adopted, and generalized for multiparticle distributions by Bohr, Heisenberg, Gordon, Jordan, Klein, Pauli, and, most significantly, by Dirac.[36]

In 1928 there appeared the greatest contribution to physical

[27] Neils Bohr, *Phil. Mag.*, 26 (1913), 1.

[28] A. Sommerfeld, *Ann. Physik*, 51 (1916), 1.

[29] H. Nagaoka, *Nature*, 69 (1904), 392.

[30] E. Rutherford, *London, Edinburgh and Dublin Phil. Mag. and J. Sci.*, 21 (1911), 669.

[31] L. de Broglie, theses (1924); *London, Edinburgh and Dublin Phil. Mag. and J. Sci.*, 47 (1924), 446.

[32] E. Schrödinger, *Collected Papers on Wave Mechanics* (London: Blackie, 1928).

[33] M. Born, *Z. Physik*, 38 (1926), 11.

[34] W. Heisenberg, M. Born and P. Jordan, *Z. Physik*, 33 (1925), 35.

[35] Max Born, *Z. Physik*, 37 (1926), 863.

[36] P. A. M. Dirac, *Proc. Phys. Soc.* (London), 112 (1926), 661; 113 (1926), 621; 114 (1927), 710; 117 (1928), 610; 118 (1928), 351.

theory of our time. Just as Newton's *Principia* forged together the five independent laws of Kepler and Galileo, all of hydrodynamics and every known fact of astronomy, ballistics, and optics,—so also did Dirac's theory of the electron unite in one formally beautiful, and experimentally powerful theory every idea of the particle physics of the Twenties. He provided a comprehensive model for the hydrogen atom, explained the Compton scattering of electrons, the Zeeman effect (doublet atoms), and the empirically required electron spin; all these independent elements were forged into an algorithm whose purpose was to achieve a relativistically invariant theory for fast electrons. Dirac's mastery is clear from his elegant adaptation of Jordan's operator calculus (itself a generalization of Heisenberg's matrix mechanics), to make the qualitative uncertainty relations a formal property of the notation. Dirac took an idea of Graves,[37] developed in Heaviside's "operational" calculus,[38] and already used in quantum theory by Born and Jordan, wherein an ordinary algebra is modified by the law $PQ-QP = n$ (some number). The properties of such a noncommutative system were well understood by 1900. But to translate this formal innovation into a systematic expression of the uncertainty relations implicit in the wave-particle fusion was pure genius. Dirac's paper established quantum mechanics as a unified description of nature. The theory's stature was even more elevated when one of its consequences—first thought a blemish by Dirac [and even earlier (1926) by Gordon,[39]]—entailed unobserved entities with queer properties. This "blemish," which Dirac,[40] Schrödinger, Weyl, and Oppenheimer[41] tried to eradicate, was seen by Blackett to describe the new antielectrons which he and Occhialini[42] and Anderson[43] observed in 1932. Dirac's theory did everything; it integrated all available facts, provided a well-formed formalism, and was fertile in

[37] Dating from 1854; referred to me by Dirac.

[38] O. Heaviside, *Electromagnetic Theory* (London, 1894–1912), Appendix K.

[39] W. Gordon, Z. *Physik*, 40 (1926), 117.

[40] P. A. M. Dirac, *Proc. Roy. Soc.* (London), 126 (1930), 360.

[41] J. R. Oppenheimer, *Phys. Rev.*, 35 (1930), 461, 562.

[42] P. M. S. Blackett and G. P. S. Occhialini, *Proc. Roy. Soc.* (London), 139 (1933), 699.

[43] Carl Anderson, *Phys. Rev.*, 41 (1932), 405.

predictions; e.g., the antiproton and the antineutron, have only recently been detected.[44]

Many early objections to, and some present groans about, the Copenhagen interpretation, arise from not appreciating the historical and conceptual role played by Dirac's paper. Here is the notational key to all subsequent quantum physics. Yet, in that paper (Dirac tells me) the Copenhagen interpretation figured essentially—not as some philosophical afterthought Dirac appends to his algebra, but basic to every operation with the notation. Feyerabend[45] provocatively suggests that this need not have been so, that it would be possible to have a "minimum" (i.e., non-Copenhagen) interpretation of quantum theory, and hence of Dirac's paper. But as a matter of fact this is not the way in which this fundamental paper was written. This would not *be* the same paper were its assumptions "purified" as Feyerabend suggests. Largely because of these tough-minded and realistically practical suppositions Dirac's theory had complete success (at least before the era of the meson). What critics of the Copenhagen interpretation often fail to see is that just to ask for an alternative account of micronature without actually providing one which works, is to reinvite the chaos which it is Dirac's triumph to have ended. The way to command a practicing physicist's attention with counter proposals is to provide a better scientific theory, not just a restatement of the orthodox formalism plus some metaphysical asides. Perhaps it *is* possible, as Feyerabend igeniously moves, to have a minimum statement of quantum theory, with no more "interpretation" than is required barely to describe the facts. But, rightly or wrongly, this is what Dirac felt he had, and what Copenhagen feels it now has, and why it views most counter proposals as observationally irrelevant superstructures. In 1952, Bohm conceded that his reinterpretation affected no known facts, but only added extra philosophical notions of heuristic value.[46] *Bohr et Heisenberg n'ont pas besoin de cette hypothèse.*

This is not to say that philosophers ought to discontinue all attempts to develop proposals which counter the Copenhagen in-

[44] E. Segrè, *Phys. Rev.*, 100 (1955) , 947; *Phys. Rev.* 101, (1956) , 909; *Phys. Rev.*, 102 (1956) , 1659; *Nuovo cimento* 3 (1956) , 447.

[45] See reference 3, p. 49.

[46] D. Bohm, *Phys. Rev.*, 85 (1952) , 166, 180.

terpretation, but only that they ought to be less enthusiastic in their own evaluations of such activity. What is certainly objectionable is introducing "reinterpretations" via references to the Copenhagen school as holding the field by a kind of authoritative dictatorship. As if there were several clearly formulable *alternative* interpretations of quantum theory which were being forcibly suppressed in favor of the naive metaphysics of personalities like Bohr and Heisenberg! This is patent nonsense. There is as yet *no* working alternative to the Copenhagen interpretation. Ask your nearest synchrotron operator. It therefore seems a questionable procedure to make every new and tentative speculation sound as if it *were* a clear alternative which could easily revolutionize the foundations of physics, if only the elder statesmen would stop backing their favorite horse so uncritically. The issue is this: *until you formulate a new interpretation which works in every particular as well as does the old one, call your efforts by their proper name, "speculations."* This makes them no less worthwhile. And if it be riposted that the Copenhagen interpretation is itself but a speculation, then please let us distinguish those speculations which have proven themselves to *work* in theory and practice from those which have not yet even been put to any rigorous test.

Consider an analogous uneasiness felt by 19th century scientists. By 1860 the inability of celestial mechanics to explain aberrations in Mercury's perihelion became obvious. Leverrier had explained the perturbations of Uranus via Newtonian mechanics by supposing another planet, "Neptune," gravitationally responsible for the anomaly. Six years later this same man detected Mercury's precession. Leverrier appealed again to the "hidden planet" hypothesis.[47] The unseen object was confidently christened "Vulcan" and made responsible for the perturbations. But Vulcan does not exist. It cannot exist (since it would require a straightline solution to the three-body problem, earth—sun—Volcan, a solution demonstrably unstable). Although many 19th century thinkers were upset by this failure, no one proposed that Newtonian astronomy be abandoned. To do that then, would have been to stop thinking about celestial phenomena altogether. One had to provide some equally useful

---

[47] U. J. J. Leverrier, *Recherches astronomiques* (L'observatoire nationale de Paris Annales, 1855–1877).

astronomy, or provisionally accept the otherwise successful orthodox theory; similarly in quantum theory (although its failings are nowhere so grave as was the Newtonian impasse).

Thus it is arguable that the Copenhagen limitations, far from being the result of philosophical naïveté, are built into the very wave-particle duality micronature has forced on us, and built also into the symmetry of explanations in terms of that duality. At least it remains clearly to be shown that this is not so. Dr. Feyerabend would not agree. He distinguishes "Born's interpretation" which gives the formalism a physical meaning, from "Bohr's interpretation" which he characterizes as being itself a metaphysical addition to the bare theory. Let us suppose that Feyerabend is correct: would it follow that "Admitting this implies that we are . . . free to invent and to consider other 'metaphysical' interpretations."?[48] Not at all! For this obscures the historical, conceptual, and operationally successful role of the Bohr view (even granting it to be "metaphysical") *as opposed to other interpretations.* The metaphysics in Newton's *Principia* is not to be rated equally with the wooley harangues of Hooke and *unintelligibilia* of Benton. The freedom for inventing alternative interpretations which Feyerabend imagines to follow on the discovery of a metaphysical strain in Bohr's view is unwarranted in the absence of an alternative formalism, and concrete experimental suggestions, on which to build the "new metaphysics."

There is a related point which concerns the experimental situation in which the quantum physicist works. An exposure to laboratory problems of microphysics (e.g., the design of apparatus) makes clear that the only way of learning about particles is to interact with them at our macrophysical level. This is not merely a comment on experimental technique. The proposition, "to learn anything about a particle we must interact with it," has the same logical force as "nothing can move faster than light," or "there cannot be a *perpetuum mobile* of the first type," or "a super-Carnot engine is nonconstructible," or "a temperature-registration of less than −273°C is impossible." None of these state *mere* matters of fact. *Each involves the conceptual principles of entire physical theories.* Similar is the proposition that one must interact with microparticles in order to learn about them. The negation of this, although not self-contradictory, is physically unintelligible.

What does this entail? Just what many philosophers of science persist in being unhappy about—that in particle physics the data can never come to us packed with invariant properties, and undistorted by the observing instrument. Data in microphysics can never be less than a compound of the microevent and some macrophysical system (a detector, or just ourselves). We have no concept of an alternative to this, as a whole cemetery of dead *gedankenexperiments* proves.[49] Such an alternative would have to rest on the possibility of using a detector whose quantum of perturbation is h, to get information about micronature in units smaller than $h!$ Interaction is *the* information concept in quantum physics. If the basic unit of interaction is h (which no hidden-variable theorist could deny), then all information patterns with which we describe the world must also be quantized in the units of h imposed by the detector. Anything "beyond" this is undetectable—unknowable. The alternative to this view can scarcely be made intelligible. Yet many early critics of quantum theory readily supposed they could have clear ideas of what electrons, and protons are "really" like, technical limitations notwithstanding. They pointed to classical statistical mechanics. There, *experimental* limitations could affect the confidence with which we described, e.g., each new thermodynamical event. But they never altered our *concepts* of the matter involved, a hidden symmetry was always felt to lurk behind the statistics. (This confidence results, of course, from confounding, e.g., "phenomenological thermodynamics" with "deductive thermodynamics," developed from the two principles of impotence.) It is however, *the* feature of experimental microphysics that the degree and manner of the perturbation of the system by the detector is *in principle* incalculable.

This situation is not novel. Let's take seriously this reference to statistical mechanics. The names of Boltzmann and Gibbs spring to mind. In his irresolvably statistical gas theory[50] Boltzmann often objects to Newtonian concepts of observation, as contrasted with

[49] W. Heisenberg, cf., his essay in *Niels Bohr and the Development of Physics* (London: Pergamon, 1955).

[50] L. Boltzmann, *Vorlesungen über gastheorie* (Leipzig: J. A. Barth, 1910).

what earlier physicists were really entitled to count as such. Boltzmann did not feel that gas theory required statistical formulation
only because of experimental limitations. No; he viewed statistical
mechanics as the primary discipline; it is directly connected with
observable parameters. Punctiform masses and ideal particle popu-
lations Boltzmann construed not as the starting point of physics,
but as abstractions of heuristic value merely: these were dubious
variables hidden within the total laboratory exploration of a physical event. They *are* notationally simpler and as such are indispensable in calculation. But the simplicity is merely formal, and should
not be in any way confounded with thinking about actual observational data. The development of kinetic theory might have proceeded more smoothly had early mechanics attended to what is
observable and not only to what is easier to conceive and calculate.
There are no *special* mechanical problems about gases other than
that they *must* be described as observed *en masse*. They will not be
experimentally or theoretically reduced to metaphysically prior
abstractions. [If one tries this, random phenomena (e.g., Brownian
motion) must be abandoned as inexplicable.] Boltzmann saw every
observation as a function of the design of the apparatus and of the
observer's knowledge of the previous state of the observed system.

A more forceful illustration, often invoked by Bohr, is Gibbs'
thermodynamics.[51] Imagine a hot metal emitting electrons. A measuring apparatus registers, by the blackening of a point on a
photographic plate, the emission of any electron with a velocity
greater than v. Now adjust the apparatus so that such electrons are
emitted but very infrequently. This type of measurement of the
metal's temperature leads to an "objective" determination of one of
its proprerties. We express this mathematically by regarding the
"metal system" as a sample arbitrarily selected from a canonical
ensemble.

But what does "objective" mean here? It means that *any* thermometer can be used as measuring instrument, and that measurements do not depend on either thermometer or observer. Now if the
total system, metal-plus-apparatus, is completely isolated from the
rest of the universe, it has a constant energy (whose value is not

[51] W. Gibbs, *Collected Works* (New Haven, Conn.: Yale University Press, 1948).

exactly known because of the canonical distribution). If, however, the metal is not isolated (as must be the case) its energy varies with time and oscillates in temperature equilibrium about a mean value as indicated by the distribution. If now the canonical ensemble of the total system follows a Newtonian pattern, the ensemble evolves, containing an increasing proportion of states in which points on the plate are blackened. The probability that the measuring apparatus will respond at a certain place at t can be calculated, but the exact instant and place of an actual event cannot be predicted. Were every detail of this experiment known at the start, *à la LaPlace*,[52] we should be able to determine beforehand each actual point-blackening, *provided that the experimental system were cut off and isolated from the rest of the universe.* But in this case the statement of the temperature would be operationally unintelligible. If, however, the experimental system is really connected with, and part of, the external world, then even complete knowledge of its details would not allow precise predictions, since we cannot possibly know every detail of the remaining universe.

This total experimental system also contains a "subjective" element, despite the assumptions of those who suppose thermodynamics to carry no thumbprints of the observing instrument. In the absence of a detecting apparatus, the descriptive mathematics of the system changes continuously, as outlined. But introject a detector; it will *suddenly* register that a point on the plate is blackened. The representation is altered discontinuously, because here we have moved from the former situation containing a great range of mathematical possibilities to a new ensemble containing only the plate blackened at one point. For *that* event, *ex post facto,* the formal statistical representation originally appropriate has no further descriptive utility. This discontinuous change is not contained or even hinted at in the Gibbs' equations characterizing the ensemble. It corresponds to the "reduction of wave packets" in quantum theory (the relevance of the Einstein-Podolsky-Rosen *gedankenexperiment* here should be clear). Thus, characterizing an *experimental* system as a Gibbs' ensemble not only specifies *its* properties, but is also contingent on an observer's knowledge of it, or (what is the same) on a detector's presence within that system. Hence the

[52] P. S. LaPlace, *Essai philosophique sur les probabilités* (Paris, 1920 ed.).

word "objective" in this context is philosophically questionable (and the same may be said of "subjective," too) .

To summarize: one can assign an "objective" temperature to a body on the evidence of the average velocity of its particles, some of which escape (altering thereby "the body") and are recorded by a detector whose own properties are inextricably involved in the "reading." Now, if one had a microphysical knowledge of the particles, one could predict every actual recording by the detector—place and time. But in that case one could no longer assign an *objective* temperature to the body, since the very concepts of temperature and entropy presuppose statistical disorder. Objective temperature and actual recordings are thus mutually exclusive, though complementary: the former requires absolute randomness. The latter, by determining an actual event, curtails randomness to that extent. Again, every such recording, by changing the ensemble, reduces the probability function in the Gibbs' representation, a reduction nowhere written in the equations of motion for the particles.

Against all this consider quantum mechanics itself. A microsystem can be represented by a wave function or by a statistical mixture of such functions (i.e., by a density matrix) . This corresponds to a Gibbs' ensemble. If the system interacts with the world, only the mixture (or matrix) representation is possible; we cannot know all details of the total macrophysical system (i.e., the universe) . If the microsystem is closed, we may have a "pure case," represented by a vector in Hilbert space. This representation is completely "objective." It contains nothing connected with any observer's knowledge or with any detector's reaction. Calculations concerning this vector are certifiably valid or invalid according to objective rules. But such a representation is completely abstract. Its various mathematical expressions $|\psi(q)|^2$, $|\psi(p)|^2$, do not refer to experimental space or to observable properties: they contain no physics whatever. The microsystem *qua* vector group in Hilbert space becomes a description of physical nature only when linked to how possible experiments will result. Here we *must* consider the interaction of the system with the measuring apparatus, the detecting instrument, the observer. We *must* use a statistical mixture in representing this joint, and discontinuously fluctuating, system.

Could this be avoided by isolating the microsystem and the observing apparatus from the macrophysical universe? No, its connection with, and placement within, the universe is a necessary condition for the apparatus to perform its intended function; its behavior must register in actual experiments if we are to get information from the apparatus. Again, this is not logical necessity. The denial of this does not reduce to $P.{\sim}P$. P-and-not-P. (If it did, we would not be discussing physics, —only the formal properties of an algorithm.) Still, this denial describes nothing intelligible. It is inconceivable ("systematically unintelligible") that we should ever encounter a *perpetuum mobile*. So also is it inconceivable that in experiment the measuring apparatus should both perform its intended function, and also be isolated from the macrophysical world. The joint system is therefore describable only a statistical mixture of wave functions—or a density matrix. It *inevitably* contains statements about the observer or the detector.

To deny this is to rob us of the very concepts needed to experiment in microphysics at all. When detectors mark certain behavior in the experiment, the mathematical representation is thereby altered discontinuously. One among various statistical possibilities has proved actually to obtain. This discontinuous "reduction of wave packets," underivable from any form of Schrödinger's equation, is (as in Gibbs' theory) an effect of shifting from mathematical descriptions to experimental actualities. That is, an actual observation reduces the original ψ representing an ensemble of possibilities of future particle behavior, to a new ψ, whose future possibilities will have been altered irreversibly by the first observation. This shift from original ψ to new ψ is not in the wave equation. One *can* imagine all this projected back in time, but never so far back that the joint system can be thought separate from the macrophysical world. (This assumption is incompatible with the validity of quantum mechanics for closed systems and hence leaves us no concept with which we can genuinely think about quantum phenomena.)

Hence a system isolated from the macrophysical world cannot be described in classical terms. We *may* say that the state of the closed system described by a Hilbert vector is objective, although it does not obtain. Here, however, the classical idea of objectivity must be abandoned for Meinongean mountains. The description of a microsystem by its Hilbert vector group complements its description in classical terms (just as a Gibbs' description of a microscopic state complements a statement of its temperature). The description of an event can be effected by classical concepts to just that approximation to quantum theory one needs for predictions in a given context; this is one version of the correspondence principle. Quantum theory can also be used however. So the boundary between object-observed and instrument-observing can be pushed indefinitely toward the latter, just as I can always regard the temperature of a body as but a property of some thermometer placed in a specified physical context containing the original body. In this case the statistical nature of the laws of microphysics is again seen to be unavoidable.

So much for the history of the Copenhagen interpretation.

II

Consider now some representative types of attack on this interpretation. The opposition has moved against Copenhagen on four fronts. The earliest discomfort concerned the statistical nature of quantum laws. How should one interpret the ψ function in the fundamental Schrödinger equation? $[\hbar/i \cdot \partial\psi/\partial t = \hbar^2/2m \nabla^2\psi$; i.e., a linear, homogeneous, partial differential equation for the de Broglie wave function $\psi(x,t)$]. In his dissertation de Broglie's *ondes de phase* are never clearly defined. Are they but algebraic fictions, or are they physical existants? His theory of the pilot wave, a wave supposed to accompany every microparticle, suggests the latter view. But no experiment has ever revealed such pilot waves in electrons, protons, or neutrons. Exit de Broglie.

Abstract configuration space is not for Schrödinger either. He imagines an infinite number of interfering Maxwell waves, whose resultant wave maximum just *is* the particle in question.[53] For him an electron is an "energy smear"; $|\psi(q)|^2$ gives the measure of the spread and intensity of that smear. This view collapses immediately in any multibody collision problem. Here Schrödinger must entertain actual spaces of an indefinite number of dimensions (for N

---

[53] Erwin Schrödinger, *Four Lectures on Wave Mechanics* (London: Blackie, 1928).

particles ψ is a function of $3N$ coordinates) —an idea with no experimental interpretation whatever (save in the "degenerate" case
of one particle, where configuration space and physical space coincide). De Broglie, Schrödinger, and also Einstein[54] and Jeffreys[55] have always contended that quantum theory has not yet
settled down. It is like mechanics in 1600, phenomenological and
chaotic. Schrödinger seeks to rewrite microphysics as a classical field
theory. Others, like Bunemann,[56] pursue hydrodynamic models in
which the singularities are localizations in a continuous substratum.
These attempts, however, have all proved disappointing so far,
which is another way of saying that at present we have in fact *one*
way of construing quantum phenomena, and this is in terms of the
orthodox Copenhagen formulation. Show the physicist a clear, detailed, physically intelligible alternative and he will readily try it.
But, in general, a physicist will use a formalism only so far as its
parameters are testable; hence he usually takes the ψ function to
measure either the probability of finding a particle within a given
volume element, or the probability that certain areas on a target
detector will be more affected by particle impact than other areas;
or ψ may be related to determinations of the density of particles
within a parallelepiped of the particle beam, etc. This doesn't mini-
mize the reality of the wave aspect of microparticles. A pencil of
β rays scattered by metal foil will leave target patterns describable
only by the distribution implicit in the ψ function of equations appropriate for β particles in such a situation. We possess direct
evidence of the correctness of de Broglie's approximation in the
diffraction of particle beams by crystal lattices. The resulting patterns obey Bragg's law and all other laws of diffraction by spatial
gratings as are observed in x-ray diffraction, and with the exact
wavelength required by the law $\hbar K = p$ ($K =$ wave propagation
vector). The "ultimate" property of individual particles responsible
for this distribution remains for the Copenhagen theorist as it might
have been for Newton: *I have not been able to discover the cause of*

54 Albert Einstein, *Science News*, 17 (1948).

55 H. Jeffreys, *Scientific Inference* (2nd ed., London: Cambridge University Press,
1957).

56 O. Bunemann, in a series of lectures and (unpublished) papers delivered
at Cambridge University.

these properties of the distribution; it is enough that a particle will more probably strike in one place rather than in another, and that I have a formula for describing.[57] Or in Bohr's own words: "The entire formalism is to be considered as a tool for deriving predictions, of definite or statistical character, as regards information obtainable under experimental conditions described in classical terms and specified by means of parameters entering into the algebraic or differential equations. . . . These symbols themselves are not susceptible to pictorial interpretation."[58]

The second charge against Bohr's view has concerned uneasiness about the uncertainty relations. But it has often been shown that this discomfort usually consists in simply misunderstanding the conceptual structure of the theory, and in failing to comprehend the reasons for our needing such a theory at all. It need only be remarked that one could generate all of quantum theory from a suitable statement of these relations alone. So they cannot be a peripheral blemish. They are the heart of quantum theory itself. How else to understand how Dirac's noncommutative operators have achieved so much?

A third discomforture concerns just this noncommutative algebra. Some can feel no confidence in a theory whose mathematics are managed according to: $QP - PQ = n$. This is reminiscent of the dissatisfaction many felt with Heaviside's decision to represent dx/dt by p, treating p as any ordinary algebraic quantity. This also lends to a noncommutativity. Critics thought the operational calculus but a sloppy approximation to some more refined-but-then-uninvented theory. Still, the calculus does its job (e.g., in alternating current circuit theory) if one learns the rules of the algorithm. Similarly the Dirac calculus: it was more powerful in prediction and in explanation of microphenomena than any previous theory. Noncommutativity *per se* is no blemish; here it is an ingenious expression of what the data oblige us to think. Landé indeed, may even have an argument which relates noncommutativity to the

[57] See reference 10, *Principia*, Conclusion: "I have not been able to discover the cause of those properties of gravity . . . it is enough that gravity does really exist, and act according to the law we have explained."
[58] N. Bohr, *Dialectica* II (1947) .

"natural" postulates of theoretical continuity and symmetry, as these arise in thermodynamics, especially the second law.[59]

There are *genuine* formal improprieties within quantum theory, e.g., "renormalization" and the unintelligible negative probabilities ("ghost states"). True, some physicists (e.g., Heisenberg) have tried to relate these mathematical inelegancies to the structure of what is fundamentally the Dirac theory. But even Heisenberg's most recent work is couched in a noncommutative algebra.

A final kind of discomfort with the Copenhagen School concerns an asymmetry in microphysical explanation and prediction. In classical physics explaining X is symmetrical with predicting X. If I explain X via the laws of a system S by reference to initial conditions α, β, γ . . . then I might as easily have predicted X on the basis of α, β, γ . . . and operating on these via the rules of S. Thus a retrogradation of Mars is explained via celestial mechanics by referring to Mars' mean angular velocity, distance from the sun, mass, and coordinates at some past time. But conversely, at this time past, to have known Mars' coordinates, mass, distance, and velocity would have allowed one to predict via S that at certain future times Mars would be in apparent retrograde movement. For those who take this as the paradigm of explanation and prediction, disappointment with the quantum-theoretic situation is inevitable. Thus Leibniz would have felt disappointment: "The mark of perfect knowledge is that nothing appears in the thing under consideration which cannot be accounted for, and that nothing is encountered whose occurrence cannot be predicted in advance."[60]

After a microphysical event X has occurred within our purview, of course, we can give a complete explanation of its occurrence within the total quantum theory. But it is in principle impossible to predict in advance those features of X so easily explained *ex post facto*. This meshes with our earlier points. Expressions of discomfort at this juncture are often just a covert way of announcing that one likes his physics deterministic, objective, orthodox,—in short, Newtonian. But then would such a one also assent to the second law of thermodynamics? If he does (and what else can he do?), is this not inconsistent, as Landé has argued, with any classical determinism?

[59] A. Landé, *Foundations of Quantum Theory* (New Haven, Conn.: Yale University Press, 1955).

[60] G. Leibniz, *De la Sagesse* (1693).

III

Heisenberg has examined in detail several typical counterinterpretations of quantum theory.[61] These fall, roughly, into four classes:

(1) The amorphous sighs of yesterday's great men who have not offered one scrap of algebra to back up their grandfatherly advice. This is all reminiscent of Hooke's annoying charge that Newton had merely provided a formula for gravity, but had said nothing about its causes; to which Newton retorted that if Hooke had some *mathematical* contribution to make, he would listen—but not to metaphysical poetry alone (Einstein, Schrödinger, von Laue, de Broglie, Jeffreys).[62]

(2) *Hidden variable* formalisms each of which ultimately destroys the symmetry properties which have been the power and glory of quantum theory (Bohm, Bopp, Fenyes).[63]

(3) Prose passages which fail to grasp the experimental necessity of interaction (Alexandrow).[64]

(4) Pure mathematics, offering no hint about what an experiment which could abrogate, e.g., the uncertainty relations would really be like (Janossy).[65]

The symmetry sacrifice is the significant consideration, however.

[61] W. Heisenberg, in *Niels Bohr and the Development of Physics* (London: Pergamon, 1955).

[62] Albert Einstein, *Library of Living Philosophers* (Evanston, Ill., 1949), Vol. 7; Erwin Schrödinger, in *Brit. J. Phil. Sci.*, 3 (1952), 109, 233; M. von Laue, *History of Modern Physics* (New York: Academic Press, 1950); *Naturwiss.*, 38 (1951), 60; L. de Broglie, *Revolution in Physics* and *La physique quantique restera-t-elle indeterministe?* (Paris: Gauthier-Villars, 1953); H. Jeffreys, *Scientific Inference* (London: Cambridge University Press, 1957).

[63] D. Bohm, *Phys. Rev.*, 85 (1952), 166, 180; *Causality and Chance in Modern Physics* (Princeton, N.J.: Van Nostrand, 1957); Bopp, *Z. Naturforsch.*, 2a (4) (1947), 202; 7a (1952), 82; 8a (1953), 6; Fenyes, *Z. Physik,* 132 (1952), 81. Bopp light-heartedly dismisses this symmetry condition which Bohr, Heisenberg, and Dirac have always treated as indispensable [*Observation and Interpretation* (London: Butterworth, 1957)]. But not only have the promised alternative systems (exclusively preferential either to particulate or undulatory notions) not yet been developed enough to have had any impact on the thought of practicing physicists, it remains difficult even to form a detailed concept of what such an alternative would be like.

[64] Alexandrow, *Doklady Akad. Nauk.*, 84 (1952), 2.

[65] Janossy, *Ann. Physik* (6) 11 (1952), 324.

These counterproposals all sacrifice symmetry in one form or another. Perhaps a Copenhagen-type interpretation is unavoidable if things like wave-particle duality and Lorentz invariance are genuine features of nature. Every known experiment tends to support this idea.[66] The theoretician always favors the theory which saves such symmetries (Yang and Lee included). Recall Schrödinger's attempt to restate the Dirac electron theory, eliminating the negative energy solutions. Both Weyl and Oppenheimer showed his attempt to vary with the choice of Lorentz frames; exit Schrödinger. If we decide thus the fate of genuine theories, why not the same criterion for interpretations of theories?[67]

[66] The recent parity experiments exposed no exception to Lorentz invariance. They only showed the impossibility of extending the "proper" Lorentz invariance (to continuous transformations), so as to include the discontinuous ("improper") mirroring transformation. In all experiments it has been immaterial whether or not the mirroring process embraced "charge configuration." The parity experiments showed that mirroring without charge configuration (particles—antiparticles) does not lead to invariant results for weak (decay) interactions. Present indications are that if mirroring is redefined to include the charge configuration (so that the mirror image of an electron is a positron), then Lorentz invariance does hold. I owe this point to Professor Konopinski.

[67] There is an analogy between this controversy and that over material implication in mathematical logic. The paradoxical features of material implication are unavoidable once its truth conditions are identified with those of $\sim p \vee q$. This is often termed the cause of the supposed error. It is easy, using well-known deductive rules, to show that $p \supset q$ and $\sim p \vee q$ are mutually deducible. The "paradox" is thus implicit in these rules. In fact, practicing logicians, and students also, never think the *rules* paradoxical. Anyone objecting to material implication, must therefore consider the rules concerning alternations, the equivalence of alternations and conjunctions, double negatives, conditional and *reductio ad absurdum* proof; and *then* say which of these he would abandon or modify and, if the latter, what modification he proposes. Similarly quantum theory. The "paradoxes" of the Copenhagen interpretation follow directly upon a cluster of experimental facts, and established formal techniques for dealing with these facts. An objector to this interpretation must also say which facts or operations on the facts he would abandon or modify, and, if the latter, what that modification should be. And here we need detailed, alogorithmic discussion, not just speculations about what might or might not become possible if only certain experimental dreams could come true. Quantum theory has not yet had its C. I. Lewis. [*Survey of Symbolic Lodge* (California: University of California Press, 1918) and with Langford, *Symbolic Logic* (New York: Appleton-Century-Crofts, Inc., 1932).]

IV

Professor Mehlberg has considered[68] Jordan's powerful argument against holding any of the early versions of the correspondence principle.[69] He rejects Jordan's reasoning by first accepting perfect correspondence between classical and quantum mechanics, and then concluding that therefore the latter cannot ultimately be limited in the "nonclassical" ways Bohr and Heisenberg have stressed. This is by now a familiar type of anti-Copenhagen argument which has been used with force, e.g., by Jeffreys.[70]

> . . . since the validity of quantum theory is . . . admitted to range over the whole physical universe, unobjectifiability would be a common feature of all physical concepts should unobjectifiability be an inescapable consequence of quantum theory. . . .
>
> . . . quantum theory also includes large scale bodies, physical concepts would become unobjectifiable throughout the physical universe and the epistemological consequences of this pervasive unobjectifiability would appear to be crippling for the whole empirical method of acquiring knowledge of physical objects on the basis of observation.

In other words, Mehlberg has adopted and exploited the sentiments explicitly expressed by Weyl:

> Thus we see a new quantum physics emerge of which the old classical laws are a limiting case in the same sense that Einstein's relativistic mechanics passes into Newton's . . . when c the velocity of light tends to ∞.[71]

Theoretical treatises intend something special when they speak thus.[72] In such contexts no one is misled. But in contexts like that of Mehlberg's remarks, misconceptions can arise. He seems to have

68 H. Mehlberg, in the symposium "Philosophical Problems of Quantum Mechanics," the May, 1958, meeting of the American Philosophical Association, Western Division.

69 P. Jordan, *Phil. Sci.*, 16 (1949).

70 H. Jeffreys, *Scientific Inference* (London: Cambridge University Press, 1957), pp. 215–221.

71 Weyl, *Philosophy of Mathematics and Natural Science* (Princeton, N.J.: Princeton University Press, 1949).

72 P. Ehrenfest, Z. *Physik*, 45 (1927), 7–8.

this perplexity: the motions of planets are described and explained in terms of "the old classical laws." In practice it is not possible to determine planetary states by sharp coordinates and momentum vectors, nor can one eliminate the observer's error. Still, it is always legitimate to speak of the planet as *having* exact coordinates and moments. In classical mechanics uncertainties in state determination are in principle eradicable. Thus *point particles are conceptual possibilities within classical particle physics.*

Within Dirac's theory however, to speak of the exact coordinates and momentum of a particle at t is to make no assertion at all. What could such an assertion consist in? That a wave packet has been compressed to a point? This cannot even be false. There is no such concept. *Point particles, therefore, are not conceptual possibilities within quantum physics.*

Yet we are told, by Weyl and Mehlberg, that quantum theory embraces classical physics as a limiting case. The justification for this is usually given in the classical connection between radiation and electrical oscillation when we consider the orbital frequency of the hydrogen atom's electron. $(\omega/2\pi = \gamma = 4\pi^2 me^4/h^3 n^3.)$ Quantum theory gives a formula for this analogous to the classical connection. $[\gamma = (2\pi^2 e^4/h^3)\ (n_i^2 - n_f^2/n_i^2 n_f^2)$ —for frequency of radiation connected with the transition $n_i \rightarrow n_f$. If this transition is small as against n_i, we write $\gamma = (4\pi^2 e^4 m/h^3 n_i^3)\ (n_i - n_f)$.] In the limiting case of large quantum numbers $\Delta N = 1$ gives a frequency identical with the classical frequency. The transition $\Delta N = 2$ gives the first harmonic.

Here a perplexity arises which may have affected Mehlberg. A cluster of symbols S expresses an intelligible assertion in classical mechanics, yet that same S does not do so in quantum mechanics. Could $(d^2s/dt^2) = d^2n/dt^2$ be transferred into Dirac's notation? No; still, classical and quantum languages are said to be continuous—arbitrarily distinguished clusters of statements in but one language.

However, statements and language don't work this way. A well-formed sentence S, if it makes an intelligible assertion in one part of a language, does so in all parts. Technical notations are defined by rules determining which symbol-combinations can make intelligible assertions. When S can express an intelligible statement here, but not there, one concludes that the languages in these contexts were different and discontinuous. Finite and transfinite arithmetics, Euclidean and non-Euclidean geometries, the language of time and the language of space, of mind and of brain; these show themselves different and discontinuous on just this principle. What may be meaningful in the one case may be unintelligible in the other. Thus $(d^2s/dt^2) = d^2n/dt^2$ may express the state of a fast particle in classical physics, but these symbols in Dirac's physics make no assertion at all. This ought to prove that the two languages are logically discontinuous. The correspondence principle apparently instructs us otherwise: quantum theory embraces the old classical laws as a limiting case. Jordan's argument, and also those of Bohr and Heisenberg, fail because microphysics "contains" macrophysics.

But how can intelligible assertions become unintelligible as quantum numbers get smaller; how do unintelligible symbol clusters become meaningful just because quantum numbers get larger? The idea of a single formula S ranging within a language from "meaningless" to "meaningful" is difficult to conceive. Either S makes an intelligible assertion throughout the language in which it figures, or else the latter is really more than one language. It's a simple matter of syntax. Either the noncommutativity of position and momentum operators holds (i.e., the S of classical physics makes no assertion whatever in quantum physics), or the correspondence principle holds (i.e., the S of classical physics is a limiting case of quantum physics). *But not both.* Or else we misconstrue one (or both) of the principles.[73] Mehlberg may have misinterpreted the second. Jordan's anticorrespondence argument should be given another hearing.

So the alternatives seem to be: (1) quantum physics cannot embrace classical physics, or (2) quantum physics is not permanently restricted as the Copenhagen interpretation suggests, or (3) classical physics itself should be regarded (à la Boltzmann) as incapable of precise state determination, just as in quantum physics. Dismiss alternative 3. We may grant with Boltzmann that it is

---

[73] The same difficulty arises in terms of probability distributions. Classical theory allows joint probabilities (in determining pairs like time-energy, and position-momentum). It allows these to increase simultaneously to the limit l. In quantum theory this is illegitimate. But as quantum numbers get larger, this illegitimacy seems to decrease and ultimately to vanish. Ergo, the same perplexity.

more faithful to actual observation. But it is a self-denying ordinance of little theoretical value. A classical mechanics *sans* punctiform masses, rigid levers, and ideal gases would be too difficult to handle to justify its purity (even so, perhaps we ought still to insist on treating rational mechanics as but an ideal abstraction out of the observationally more fundamental statistical mechanics). Alternative 2 we have already considered.

I suggest there is no ultimate *logical* connection between classical physics and quantum physics, any more than between a sense datum language and a material object language. Consider: the punctiform mass, a primarily kinematical idea, is the springboard of classical theory. The wave pulse, a primarily dynamical idea, is the fountainhead of quantum theory. Languages springing from such different stock will show this difference throughout their whole structure. Notwithstanding the correspondence principle, the languages of classical and quantum mechanics diverge.

Suppose I am charged to say how hydrogen atoms with large quantum numbers behave as they do? Well, this example, and others, may be misunderstood. Such different conceptual structures cannot simply mesh in this way just because of physical facts. Their logical gears are not of the same type. Propositions get their force from the total language system in which they figure. That a particular formula gives a classical frequency for the transition $\Delta N = 1$ in the case of the hydrogen atom's electron proves at most that there are *formal analogies between certain reaches of quantum theory and certain reaches of classical theory.* That this is only an analogy is obscured by the fact that identical symbols, "$4\pi^2 me^4/h^3 n^3$," are used here in both languages. This is not more a logical identity than the uses of "$+$" and "$-$" for both valence theory and number theory shows these to have an identical logic with respect to addition and subtraction. Permit an analogy.

Men are made of cells. Whereas it is true to assert that men have brains, personalities, financial worries, it might be no assertion at all to say such things of cells, especially if cell-talk were constructed *ab initio* as logically different from man-talk, —a move similar to the Jordan-Dirac formulation of quantum theory. The two idioms could then never merge. "It has schizophrenia and an overdrawn account" would express nothing in such a circumscribed cell-language. Even though a complex conspiracy of cells could be spoken of in ways analogous to how we speak of a man, this would not conflate the two languages, not even when both idioms characterize the same object, e.g., me. If someone speaks of me as a man but another speaks of me as a collection of cells, although the *denotatum* of both discourses be identical, the two speakers diverge conceptually. They are not speaking the same language; the logic of their speech differs. The two languages are no more identified than wave mechanics and matrix mechanics are proved identical just because the observable consequences of the one are isomorphic with those of the other. The structures of the Schrödinger and Heisenberg systems differed (as did their interpretations).[74] These differences are logical, and independent of the facts that such utterances may be made truly in superficially similar contexts, and may even be expressed in the same symbols. The continuity suggested by incautious statements of the correspondence principle may be illusory. I do not claim that it *is* illusory, but only that the matter is too rarely discussed. An exception is the work of Jordan.

So perhaps the correspondence principle does not make classical physics a limiting case of quantum physics, even though the two formalisms are completely analogous at points. What the principle does show is that when quantum numbers are high the hydrogen atom can be regarded either as a small macrophysical body set in a classical space-time, or as a large "quantum body" exemplifying to but a vanishing degree the dynamics of elementary particles. In the first case S[e.g., $(d^2r/dt^2 = d^2n/dt^2)$] will constitute an assertion. In the second case it will not. Against this Dr. Feyerabend offers a most unconvincing argument.[75] "We may," he says, "admit that macroscopic systems can be described in terms of wave functions if we assume at the same time that a macroscopic observer has never enough information at his disposal in order to set up such a wave function." Feyerabend makes it sound as if *"never having enough information to set up a macroscopic wave function"* is like *"never having enough information to verify assertions about the moon's far*

74 P. Bergmann, *Basic Theories of Physics* (Englewood Cliffs, N.J.: Prentice-Hall, 1951), p. 277.
75 P. Feyerabend, in *Observation and Interpretation* (London: Butterworth, 1957), p. 127.

side." But there is a difference in principle here which parallels just that difference between quantum and classical languages I have marked. We never *could* have enough information of the sort Feyerabend remarks. And it is in the very logic of this "never could" that the Copenhagen interpretation lives.

We may treat the hydrogen atom as we please, we may interchange Poisson brackets for quantum brackets when we wish, depending on our problem. But it need not follow that there is a logical staircase running from regions of the order of 10^{-13} cm to 10^{-13} light year. There may be one logical break; that is why we can make assertions about the exact state of Mars, but not about the elementary particle nearest Mars' classical center of gravity. As an indication of how quantum *mathematics* can be managed, the correspondence principle is clear. But when treated as by Professor Mehlberg, it might mislead. Hence I cannot agree that the anti-correspondence argument fails. It fails only if one takes the correspondence principle over-literally. But we can continue to allow chemists and engineers to treat their data realistically. This is just how the quantum physicist regards his laboratory apparatus, even while insisting on a Copenhagen interpretation for the foundations of the theory. Just as the uncertainty principle holds no consequences for ballistics (bullet's uncertainty in position = 10^{-28} cm) so quantum theory as a whole need have no conceptual consequences for classical mechanics. Certainly no physicist is *obliged* to generalize quantum physics as Mehlberg and Weyl do.

V

Finally, I would distinguish *Philosophical Problems of Quantum Mechanics* from another subject: *Problems of Philosophers Concerning Quantum Mechanics*. It is a sociological fact that most working quantum physicists do not bother with general problems concerning, e.g., the interpretation of the ψ function, not to mention the abstract philosophical matters recently raised concerning "realistic" or "nonrealistic" interpretations of quantum theory as a whole. This is not because the working physicist refuses to have, or is intellectually incapable of having, philosophical problems; he has plenty. One cannot be exposed to current discussions in quantum field theory and meson theory without feeling their logical, analytical character. This is not imported into physics from other academic contexts. I remember a discussion between Dirac, Heisenberg, and Bethe concerning whether an otherwise successful algorithm containing inconsistencies (as does renormalization) requires immediate examination—or whether danger looms only when predictions of such a theory fail. Historically this is a conceptually significant problem: remember the aether! Another is the question of interpreting the so-called "negative probabilities." Heisenberg argues that their existence in a renormalized calculation indicates a flaw in the very technique and approach to quantum theory set out in the Dirac notation. (Renormalization requires non-Hermitean operators which ruin the unitary character of the scattering matrices, require negative probabilities, and invoke physically unintelligible "ghost" states.) Others (e.g., Bethe, Peierls, Hamilton, and Salam) appraise the matter wholly differently.

Another physical practice of philosophical interest is Gell-Mann's almost taxonomical attack on meson theory. Much of the Dirac theory is unsatisfactory in this region. So Gell-Mann has proceeded like Linneaus, or Mendeléeff, or indeed, even like a natural historian—drawing up "phenomenological" charts of particle properties and allowing generalizations to stand forth from the data. Methodologists' morals about physical theory cannot ignore this "John Stuart Mill"-type approach. Despite Toulmin's campaign, it does exist in physics and can be important.[76] Many such difficulties are the daily fare of practicing quantum physics. I only point to their existence to mark how little attention philosophers pay them. This is no reason for philosophers to cease talking about what they wish. But no one should think that because most quantum physicists are unperturbed by the type of question brought to prominence by Bohm, that therefore they are unreflective, resigned, Berkleyan, computer-ridden predicting machines. What the practicing physicist is likely to find difficult in many philosophical papers concerning the foundations of quantum theory, is a facile use of terms like "realism," "objectivism," and "subjectivism." One might actually be inclined to suppose that philosophers had settled what a

[76] S. E. Toulmin, *The Philosophy of Science* (London: Hutchinson, 1953) .

discussion of realism, objectivism, and subjectivism was a discussion about. Which reminds me of the question with which an Oxford undergraduate once staggered his tutor: "What is the external world *external to?*" When I see the full sense, or nonsense, in that question, I may see also how quantum theory is going to help, or be helped by, the cracking of such old philosophical chestnuts.

8

Professor Bohm's Philosophy of Nature

by PAUL K. FEYERABEND

EDITORIAL NOTE: *The two final essays in this collection carry the story forward into the 1960's and show the argument in theoretical physics entering a new phase. As physics, it is a period of fresh uncertainties. The calm confidence of the late 1920's and early 1930's —that Dirac's mathematical equations as applied to electrons and protons (together with a small number of second-class particles) would suffice to account for the whole pageant of physical phenomena—has evaporated, and nobody cares any longer to bet on what the basic concepts of physics will be like in the year 2050. Philosophically speaking, on the other hand, theoretical physics has returned in its methods and ambitions to something more like the "mainstream," as Max Planck attempted to define it in the opening essay.*

Paul Feyerabend's essay deals with the broader philosophical issues in a liberal-minded way. He makes some important points: reminding us, for instance, that Bohr and the other Copenhagen physicists had always oscillated between claiming (moderately) that "complementarity" and the other special features of quantum mechanics were inalienable characteristics of any physics consistent with Heisenberg's basic ideas, and claiming (more daringly) that these features were inescapable features of all future physical theories having any serious claim on our attention. Starting from a position very close to that of Niels Bohr, David Bohm had ended by seeing that only the former, more moderate claims was at all defensible. Similarly, Heisenberg's rejection of the label "positivist" was the result of a confusion of terms. All he in fact disowned was Mach's earlier "sensationalist" version of positivism, in favor of the "physi-calist" position of the later Vienna Circle philosophers which finds its epistemological basis in a different set of "hard data" (viz., "pointer-readings" rather than "sense data") but is just as skeptical about speculative theories involving the imaginative construction of new models for interpreting these data.

On the other hand, Feyerabend hesitates to follow Bohm in laying it down—as a matter of cosmological principle, so to speak—that nature must be infinitely rich in levels of analysis and complexity. As a pupil of Karl Popper, he is content to treat such alleged prin-ciples as provisional hypotheses, which cannot be held as general maxims but must be exposed to critical testing and possible falsi-fication, taking their chance along with all other such hypotheses. Still, over the crucial methodological point he and Bohm are at one: that the orthodox Copenhagen position—when adopted enthusiasti-cally, as laying down limits on all future systems of physics—had at-tempted to impose a premature cloture on scientific debate, of a sort that was epistemologically unwarranted. Physicists might set up cer-tain intellectual ideals for themselves, such as the "progressive elimination of anthropomorphous elements" called for by Max Planck; but the improvement of theory remained a "progressive" affair, with Truth—like Kant's Ding-an-Sich—at best an ideal limit toward which we approximate in an asymptomatic manner.

I

THIS IS a belated review of a highly interesting and thought pro-voking book.[1] Although dealing with some difficulties of a very specialised theory of today, viz. of the quantum theory, it should yet be of interest to the many non-physicists who want to know about the world we live in as well as about the ideas which are at present being developed for understanding this world. It is often assumed—and the basic philosophy of many contemporary physicists supports this assumption—that within the sciences speculation and ingenuity cannot play a very great role as physical theories are more or less uniquely determined by the facts. It is of course also assumed that our present knowledge about the microcosm is determined in

---

[1] David Bohm, *Causality and Chance in Modern Physics* (Princeton, N.J.: Van Nostrand, 1957; London: Routledge, 1957).

exactly this way and therefore irrevocable, at least in its main features. The book shows that this is not correct, it shows that today there exists a clash of ideas about some very fundamental things, that the imposing and perhaps a little terrifying picture of science of an unalterable and steadily increasing collection of facts is nothing but a myth, and that ingenuity and speculation play in physics as great a role as anywhere else. It also shows that even now it is possible to present difficult matters in an interesting and understandable way. It shows thereby that the separation, so often deplored, between the sciences and the humanities is due to a false picture, if not a caricature of science. It is this false picture which is attacked throughout the book. More especially, the book contains an explicit refutation of the idea that complementarity and complementarity alone solves all the ontological and conceptual problems of microphysics; that this solution possesses absolute validity; that the only thing left to the physicist of the future is to find, and to solve equations for the prediction of events which are otherwise well understood. In short, it contains a refutation of the idea that the physicist of the future is bound to be very similar to the more dogmatic of the medieval scholars with the sole exception that Bohr, and not Aristotle, will be his authority in matters metaphysical.

Secondly, the book presents, in qualitative terms, a new interpretation of some microphysical theories, and especially of the elementary quantum-theory of Schrödinger and Heisenberg. It attempts to develop, again in qualitative terms, a general picture of the universe which can give an account of statistical phenomena without assuming that they are irreducible. It discusses, on the basis of the picture presented, such fundamental problems of scientific method as the problem of induction, and the problem of the validity of empirical generalisations and of universal theories. Doing this without any discussion of "ordinary language" or of language systems it (implicitly) [2] refutes another idea that is very fashionable today, viz. the idea that the only fruitful way of discussing more general problems of knowledge is either to analyse

---

2 Cf. also the explicit discussion of the merits of conceptual analysis in [156]. (*Note:* numbers in square brackets refer to pages of the book under review.)

"ordinary" language (whatever that may mean), or to construct formal systems and to investigate their properties.

Having expressed in the above two paragraphs, as I hope I have done, that I consider Bohm's book a major contribution to the contemporary philosophy of nature I must at once add that there are many things in it which I cannot accept and that more especially his discussion of the problem of induction seems to me to be highly unsatisfactory. Bohm's physical ideas are original, refreshing, and sorely needed in a time of complacency with respect to fundamentals. But the philosophical standpoint taken up with respect to both physics and cosmology is traditional, and perhaps even reactionary: it is a curious mixture of the methodological doctrine of inductivism and of ideas which may be found in various dialectical philosophies. This will become evident from a more detailed investigation of the book.

II

In order to enter into Bohm's theory, I will first discuss the Copenhagen point of view. When it was first conceived this point of view constituted an interpretational feat of great importance. One realises this when the historical situation is considered a little more closely. The early quantum theory of Bohr and Sommerfeld, although experimentally very successful, was yet regarded as unsatisfactory by many physicists. Its main fault was seen to lie in the fact that it combined classical and non-classical assumptions in a way that made a coherent interpretation impossible. For many physicists it was nothing more than a stepping stone on the way to a really satisfactory theory, i.e. to a theory which could give us not only correct predictions, but also some insight into the nature and the dynamics of microscopic entities. It is quite true that Bohr, Heisenberg, and others worked along very different lines. Their main objective was not the construction of a new physical theory about a world that existed independently of measurement and observation; their main objective was rather the construction of a logical machinery for the utilisation of those parts of classical physics which could still be said to lead to correct predictions. Quite obviously a theory of this latter type does not admit of a realistic interpretation:

the classical signs it contains cannot be interpreted realistically as they are no longer universally applicable. And the non-classical signs it contains cannot be interpreted realistically as they are elements of the logical machinery used for the purpose of prediction, and possess no meaning apart from that usage. However that may be—the philosophical spirit behind the "Korrespondenzdenken" was by no means shared by everybody. Now the most important thing is that Schrödinger's wave mechanics, which was conceived in an entirely different spirit, and which seemed to present the long awaited new and coherent account of the microscopic entities, encountered peculiar difficulties when the attempt was made to connect it with a universal interpretation of the kind that was applicable to the earlier theories. Any attempt to interpret wave mechanics as descriptive of entities which, although possessing new and surprising features, were still elements of an objective physical universe, any such attempt was found to lead to paradoxical consequences. It was Bohr's great merit that in this situation he developed an intuitive idea, the *idea of complementarity,* which, although incompatible with a straightforward realism, nevertheless gave the physicists a much needed intuitive aid for the handling of concrete problems.

According to this idea properties can be ascribed to a microscopic system only when it interacts with a suitable classical (i.e. macroscopic) piece of matter. Apart from the interaction the system possesses no properties at all. It is also asserted that the totality of classical measuring-instruments[3] divides into pairs of kinds which are mutually incompatible in the following sense: if the system under investigation interacts with a measuring instrument which belongs to one of two mutually incompatible kinds, then all the properties defined by interaction with the other kind will be wholly undertermined. And "wholly undetermined" means that it would be meaningless to ascribe such a property to the system just as it would be meaningless to ascribe to a fluid a certain value on the Mohs scale of scratchability. It is clear that the *uncertainty relations* now indicate the domain of permissible applicability of classical

---

[3] This totality comprises pieces of matter which have not been prepared by a physicist for the purpose of measurement, but which, by accident, as it were, satisfy some very general conditions not to be discussed here.

functors (such as the functor "position") rather than the mean deviations of their otherwise well defined values in large *ensembles*. The idea of complementarity can be interpreted in two different ways. It can be interpreted as an attempt to provide an intuitive picture for an existing theory, viz. wave mechanics, and as a heuristic principle guiding future research. This interpretation is undogmatic as it admits the possibility of alternatives, and even of preferable alternatives. A physicist who looks at complementarity in this way will regard it as an interesting fact about quantum theory that it is *compatible* with a relational point of view where interaction is a necessary condition of the meaningful applicability of terms which within classical physics (relativity included) are definable without such reference. He will also point out that there exist no satisfactory alternatives. But he will never go as far as to assert that such alternatives will never be found, or that they would be logically inconsistent, or that they would contradict the facts. But Bohr's idea of complementarity can also be interpreted in a different way. It can be interpreted as a basic philosophical principle which is incapable of refutation and to which any future theory *must* conform. Bohr himself most certainly took this stronger point of view. "Thus rather than consider the indeterminacy relationships primarily as a deduction from quantum mechanics in its current form he postulates these relationships directly as a basic law of nature and assumes . . . that all other laws will have to be consistent with these relationships" [83, referring to Heisenberg]. His assumption was "that the basic properties of matter can *never* be understood rationally in terms of unique and unambiguous models" which implies that "the use of complementary pairs of imprecisely defined concepts will be necessary for the detailed treatment of every domain that will ever be investigated" [94]. It is true that some followers of the Copenhagen school have denied that this absolutism is part of complementarity. Thus in a discussion Rosenfeld has asserted that "nobody thinks of attributing an absolute validity to the principles of quantum theory."[4] But quite apart from the fact that he himself said in the lecture preceding this

---

[4] Rosenfeld, *Observation and Interpretation,* ed. Körner (London: Butterworth, 1957) , p. 52.

discussion that "every feature" of the theory "is forced upon us,"[5] there is Bohr's explicit statement that "it would be a misconception to believe that the difficulties of the atomic theory may be evaded by eventually replacing the concepts of classical physics by new conceptual forms."[6]

III

This dogmatism with respect to fundamental principles is attacked and refuted in Chapter III of Bohm's book. The chapter contains an extremely lucid description of the development of the quantum theory and the various interpretations which have been suggested for it. It explains the reasonable elements of the point of view of Bohr and Heisenberg. This point of view is presented with a clarity that is sadly missing in many writers who support Bohr, and with an understanding, and authority that reveals the former follower and expositor[7] of Bohr's ideas. The idea of its final and absolute validity is refuted by showing that all attempts to prove it (as indeed all attempts of a "transcendental deduction" of physical principles) are circular. Thus, in Heisenberg's "proof" of the uncertainty principle (which is often used as an argument for its absolute validity)

> it was essential to use three properties; namely the quantization of energy and momentum in all interactions; the existence of these quanta; and the unpredictable and uncontrollable character of certain features of the individual quantum process. It is certainly true that these properties follow from the quantum theory [94].

However in order to show the basic and irrefutable character of the uncertainty principle these features themselves would have to be demonstrated as basic and irrefutable. Quite obviously such a demonstration cannot be achieved by pointing to some theorems of *wave mechanics* (such as von Neumann's theorems) as this would only lead to the further question whether wave mechanics is valid

---

5 *Ibid.*, p. 41.

6 N. Bohr, *Atomic Theory and the Description of Nature* (Cambridge, 1932), p. 16.

7 Cf. Bohm, *Quantum Theory* (Princeton, N.J.: 1951).

in all domains of experimentation [95]. Nor can it be achieved, as has been attempted by many inductivists, by utilising the fact (if it is a fact) that either wave mechanics, or some part of it, is highly confirmed. In order to see this most clearly we need only realise that the assertion of the absolute validity of a physical principle implies the denial of any theory that contains its negation. More especially, the assertion of the absolute validity of the uncertainty principle implies the denial of any theory that ascribes to it only a limited validity in a restricted domain. But how could such a denial be justified by *experience* if the denied theory is so constructed that it gives the same predictions as the defended principle wherever the latter has been found to be confirmed by experience?[8]

It follows that neither experience nor mathematics can help if a decision is to be made between wave mechanics and an alternative theory which agrees with it in all those points where the latter has been found to be empirically successful. Now the idea of complementarity is well fitted to the structure of wave mechanics. As we cannot make any restrictions upon the structure of the empirically satisfactory alternatives of wave mechanics it also follows that its interpretation as a basic and irrefutable principle must be given up. Neither mathematics nor experience can be used to support such an interpretation. All this means, of course, that the position of complementarity is a metaphysical position[9] which can be defended by arguments of plausibility only.

[8] Quantum mechanics is not the first theory that has been utilised for the purpose of excluding alternatives. Using the fact that certain theorems of Newtonian mechanics contradicted the second law of thermodynamics, Ostwald and Mach argued that a mechanical account of heat was impossible, and that Newton's laws could not be universally vaild. It turned out, however, that it was the second law that was not universally valid (fluctuations). Quite clearly the Ostwald-Mach argument suffered from the same deficiency as the more recent arguments of Born, Rosenfeld, and others. They argued: the second law is highly confirmed; classical mechanics contradicts the second law; hence classical mechanics is not universally valid. They overlooked (*a*) that confirmation does not imply truth; (*b*) that the mechanical theory of heat contradicted the second law in a domain in which it had not yet been tested, and in which it was therefore neither confirmed nor disconfirmed.

[9] I use here the word "metaphysical" in the same sense in which it is used by the adherents of the orthodox point of view, viz. in the sense of "neither mathematical, nor empirical." That the Copenhagen interpretation is metaphysical in this sense has been asserted, in slightly different words, by Heisenberg who declared in 1930 (*Die physikalischen Grundlagen der Quantentheorie*, p. 15), that its adoption was a "question of taste." This he repeated in 1958 in the now more

IV

So far only the (empirical and logical) *possibility* of alternative points of view has been shown. In Chapter IV of his book Bohm turns to the discussion of some alternatives that have actually been proposed in the literature and he also expounds some of his own ideas. I shall now give an outline of the epistemological background of all these alternatives.

One of the basic assumptions of the orthodox is that "in our description of nature the purpose is . . . to trace down, as far as it is possible, relations between the manifold aspects of our experience."[10] For them the facts of experience play the role of building stones out of which a theory may be constructed but which themselves neither can, nor should be modified. If we add to this the idea that "only with the help of classical ideas is it possible to ascribe an unambiguous meaning to the results of observation"[11] (which means that the building stones referred to in the first quotation are classical states of affairs) we arrive at once at the result that a microscopic theory cannot be anything but a device for the prediction of a particular kind of fact, viz. of classical states of affairs. Now it is quite true that this point of view has led to some useful results (example: the dispersion formula of Ladenburg-Kramers; the first investigations of Heisenberg). It is also true that the quantum theory is the first theory of importance which to some extent satisfies the programme of Berkeley and Mach (classical states of affairs replacing the "perceptions" of the former and the

fashionable linguistic terminology (cf. *Physics and Philosophy* [New York 1958], pp. 29 ff). However at the very same place a highly objectionable criticism is found of Bohm's model of 1952. This model, it is asserted, "cannot be refuted by experiment since [it] only repeat[s] the Copenhagen interpretation in a different language. From a strictly positivistic standpoint" Heisenberg continues "one may even say that we are here concerned not with counterproposals to the Copenhagen interpretation, but with its exact repetition in a different language." Is it really the case that Bohm's counterexample against the assertion, made by von Neumann and others, that quantum theory does not allow for the addition of *untestable* hidden parameters (cf. von Neumann, *Mathematical Foundations of Quantum Mechanics* [Princeton, N.J.: 1955], p. 326) is nothing but the "exact repetition" of this assertion "in a different language"?

[10] Bohr, *op. cit.*, p. 18.

[11] *Ibid.*, p. 17.

"elements" of the latter). But it must not be forgotten that there is a whole tradition which is connected with the philosophical position of realism[12] and which went along completely different lines. In this tradition the facts of experience, whether or not they are now describable in terms of a universal theory (such as classical mechanics), are not regarded as unalterable building stones of knowledge; they are regarded as capable of analysis, of improvement, and it is even assumed that such an analysis and improvement is absolutely necessary. Indeed, the new theory of motion which was developed by Galileo and Newton could not possibly be understood as a device for establishing "relations between the manifold aspects of our experience," the simple reason being that, according to this very theory, observable motion would at best give us an approximation to its fundamental laws. Similarly the atomic theory of the late nineteenth century was not only not suggested, it was even contradicted by what was then regarded as an account of "experience," viz. classical thermodynamics. This tradition proceeds from the very reasonable assumption that our ideas *as well as* our experiences may be erroneous and that the latter give us at most an approximative account of what is going on in reality. Bohm's own point of view is closely connected with this tradition. Having shown that all the attempts to prove the uniqueness of the Copenhagen interpretation are invalid, he suggests "to take the field and particle concepts of classical physics as starting points and to *modify* and enrich them in such a way that they are able to deal with the new combination of wave and particle properties that is implied in the quantum theory" [98; my italics]. Such modified concepts, or even a completely new conceptual apparatus which does not any more make use of classical ideas, will of course at first be "extraphysical" [99] in the sense that it will not be accessible to test with the help of methods available *before* it was conceived. However "the history of scientific research is full of examples in which it was very fruitful indeed to assume that certain objects and elements might be real, long before any procedures were known that could permit them to be observed directly" [99]. Assumptions of this kind then

---

[12] For this connection cf. K. R. Popper's article "The Aim of Science," *Ratio,* 1 (1958).

ultimately lead to new kinds of experiments and thus to the discovery of new facts. In the light of this historical experience [Bohm continues] positivism (i.e. the point of view expressed in the two above quotations) is seen to lead to a one sided point of view of the possible means of carrying out research. For while it recognizes the importance of the empirical data, positivism flies into the face of the historically demonstrable fact that the proposal of new concepts and theories having certain speculative aspects (e.g. the atomic theory) has quite frequently turned out to be as important in the long run as empirical discoveries have been [99].

In this way positivism "constitutes a dogmatic restriction of the possible forms of future experience" which in the case of quantum mechanics leads to the belief

that the success of probabilistic theories of the type of the current quantum mechanics indicates that in the next domain it is very likely that we shall be led to theories that are . . . even more probabilistic than those of the current quantum domain [104].[13]

V

More concretely, Bohm's ideas as presented in the book under review may be regarded as an adaptation, to the case of the quantum theory, of the situation described by the classical kinetic theory of matter. The kinetic theory was an attempt to give an explanation, in terms of the motion of small, and as yet unobserved, particles, of the behaviour of thermodynamic systems. According to this theory continuous improvement of the precision of measurements will lead to the following phenomena (we assume that we move outside the domain where relativistic effects become noticeable) : as long as we are dealing with large systems the classical laws of motion (and the second law of thermodynamics) will be found

[13] A terminological remark: quantum physicists have sometimes refused to be called "positivists" on account of the fact that they accepted the Copenhagen point of view. Thus in *Niels Bohr and the Development of Physics* (London, 1955) , p. 22, Heisenberg asserts that "the Copenhagen interpretation . . . is in no way positivistic. For whereas positivism is based upon the sensual perceptions of the observer . . . the Copenhagen interpretation regards things and processes which are describable in terms of classical concepts . . . as the foundation of any physical interpretation." This is quite true. However this "foundation" is again assumed to be "given" in the sense that it cannot be further analysed or explained, an attitude which to a certain extent still justifies the term "positivism."

to hold with absolute precision. However when experimenting with fairly small systems such as dust-particles which are immersed into a surrounding medium, a completely new type of behaviour becomes apparent. These particles experience random displacements for which no explanation can be given in terms of the movements of bodies of a similar size. The laws describing this type of behaviour are not any longer the laws of classical mechanics. They are purely probabilistic and allow us to predict averages in large *ensembles* rather than individual processes. Within the framework of these laws no reason can be given for the occurrence of a particular movement of a particular particle. It can even be shown [107] that for particles under the conditions described above there exists laws which are formally identical with the uncertainty relationships, the diffusion constant of the embedding medium taking the place of Planck's constant h. But the situation changes again when we further improve the precision of our measurements or else use experiments of an altogether different type. We shall then find that the random behaviour of the dust particles is explainable in terms of a new set of causal laws referring to very small particles which are the ultimate constituents of the medium in which the dust-particles are immersed. (In the case of the kinetic theory these new laws happen to coincide with the laws of classical mechanics from which we started. However it is necessary to point out, in accordance with Bohm's more general ideas, that this need not always be the case.)

Speaking more generally one may now say that according to the kinetic theory there exist three different levels of experimentation which are characterised by three different sets of laws. There is the macroscopic level where the laws of classical mechanics hold exactly. More precise experiments show then that these laws are not universally valid, and thereby delimit the domain of their applicability. At the same time they lead to a new set of laws governing phenomena which are *qualitatively* different from the phenomena we meet on the macrolevel, as they involve randomness. These new laws in their turn are not universally valid as they can be shown to be the result of the very complex, but again causal behaviour of entities on a still deeper level.

Now it is Bohm's contention that the situation in the domain of the quantum phenomena is similar to the one just described. As opposed to the opinion of the majority of physicists he assumes that the probability laws of the present quantum theory are the result of the very complex interplay of entities on a deeper level, and are therefore neither ultimate nor irreducible. Chapter IV contains a general discussion of various ways in which such a sub–quantum-mechanical level can be conceived. These considerations have been criticised by some members of the Copenhagen circle. One of the most frequent criticisms is that nobody has yet succeeded in constructing a theory along these lines which can match the customary theory in predictive success. This criticism seems to proceed from the assumption that the existence of a certain theory and the absence of a theory, which is connected with a different "ideology" as it were, may be regarded as an implicit criticism of the latter. However the fact that this pragmatic criticism can also be directed against the dynamical investigations of Galileo and Kepler (the successful theory being in this case Aristotle's theory of motion) should be sufficient to make its proponents a little more cautious about its force. A second criticism points out that the present theories, and the philosophical structure connected with them, are firmly based upon experience. This criticism has already been dismissed in an earlier part of the present review. Indeed, we have seen that the customary point of view about microphysics cannot produce any empirical or logical argument against a procedure such as Bohm's. And assertions such as "it is idle to 'hope' that the cure of our troubles will come from underpinning quantum theory with some deterministic substratum" can at most be regarded as affirmations of faith.[14]

---

[14] Rosenfeld, in *Observation and Interpretation*, p. 44. In his review of the present book in the *Manchester Guardian*, L. Rosenfeld accused Bohm of contradicting the "exigencies of sound scientific method" and he described the followers of Niels Bohr (and presumably also himself) as possessing the "uncommitted, commonsense attitude of the true scientist." Now first of all an attitude can hardly be called "uncommitted" if it appeals to the principle that experience alone can be the judge of our theories, and at the same time is singled out neither by experience, nor by mathematics. Secondly the history of science has given ample evidence for the fact that it is "sound scientific method" not to take experience at its face value, even if it should be expressed in very complicated (classical) terms, but to try to explain it as the result of processes which are not immediately accessible to observation. It is strange indeed to see that Rosenfeld describes as "uncommitted" the attitude of those who because of their observationalistic bias distort both history and scientific method.

VI

I leave now the physics of the book and turn to a discussion of the cosmology and methodology developed in it. Both these fields are dealt with on the basis of a generalisation of the situation described by the kinetic theory. The cosmological generalisation, as I understand it, is as follows: the world contains infinitely many levels. Each level is characterised by a set of laws which may be causal, or probabilistic, or both. The validity of these laws need not extend beyond the level to which they belong. When a certain level is left qualitatively new processes appear which have to be described by a new set of laws. Bohm recognises that sometimes these new laws may be general enough to allow for the derivation of the more specific laws of the preceding level (example: special relativity—general relativity; cf. [141]). However he points out—and this must be regarded as a highly important contribution to cosmology—that such a reduction need not always be possible. Let us assume, for example, that the level L_1 of causal laws possesses a substratum L_2 of probability laws which are the outcome of the causal interplay of entities of a level L_3 which in its turn possesses a probabilistic substratum L_4, and so on. Now the fact that the laws of L_2 can be explained by reference to complicated causal mechanisms on L_3 shows that they cannot be entirely random. On the other hand the laws of L_3 are not absolutely causal either as they are limited by the fluctuations which appear upon L_4. A complete explanation of the laws of L_1 (or of any set of causal laws or of probability laws) would therefore have to take into account an infinity of laws and levels. Clearly, then, an explanation of the laws of L_1 in terms of a finite sequence of substrata cannot be regarded as a *reduction* of L_1 to these substrata. Each level, and each set of laws possesses a surplus over and above any finite set of more general laws. It is only if we take all the mutually irreducible properties and laws together that we may hope to get a complete account of one particular level. This is the way in which Bohm makes physical sense of the idea of emergence and the irreducibility of qualities. At the same time it is suggested, at least by the cosmological model we are discussing at the present moment, that qualities may be reducible after all if only appropriate mathematical instruments are found for the handling of infinites of relatively self-contained experimental domains. The model also suggests a new interpretation of the difficult problems of probability, randomness, and statistical independence. In this interpretation neither the idea of a deterministic law, nor the idea of randomness is given absolute preference [20 f.]. The laws of nature, whether they appear in the form of causal laws, or in the form of probability laws are regarded as a Hegelian synthesis, as it were, of the idea of absolute determination (the thesis), and of absolute randomness (the antithesis). This way of describing Bohm's procedure is by no means a mere verbal trick, for it is Bohm's conviction that in all fields the alternative use of opposite sets of concepts is to be preferred to the exclusive utilisation of only one of them.

VII

However, the model which we have just described and which plays an important role in Bohm's analysis of probability is not the one he uses in his discussion of scientific method. He is "not even supposing that the general pattern of levels that has been so widely found in nature thus far must necessarily continue without limit." He admits the possibility that "even the pattern of levels itself will eventually fade out and be replaced by something quite different" [139]. The structure of levels, he asserts, is only one way in which the *qualitative infinity of nature* may represent itself to the experimenter. This qualitative infinity of nature is one of the basic postulates of Bohm's cosmology. He incessantly insists upon the "inexhaustible *depth* in the properties and qualities of matter" [138] which is such that no finite system of laws and categories can ever express it adequately. Every thing and every process has infinitely many sides to it which are such that at any stage of scientific development they will only approximately be expressed by the laws and the concepts then in use. That such an approximate representation is at all possible is due to the further fact that there exists "some degree of autonomy and stability" in the mode of being of the things around us [139]. For example we may say that [a] real fluid is enormously richer in qualities and properties than is our macroscopic concept of it. It is richer, however, in just such a way that these additional characteristics may, in a wide variety of cases, be ignored in the macrodomain [155].

In spite of the fact that in every real fluid an infinite variety of processes is going on which are not covered by our macroscopic description of it, these processes just so counterbalance each other that relative stability is achieved upon the macrolevel, and the macroscopic description is in this way made applicable within its proper domain of validity. In short: the world is infinite as regards the properties and processes which are present in every part of it. But these properties are arranged in complexes of relative stability which may then be described with the help of scientific theories employing a finite number of concepts only. Every such description is true within a certain domain of validity. On the other hand the presence of further properties which are not covered by the description, and which slightly influence the elements of the complex implies that

associated with any given law there must be errors that are essential and objective features of that law resulting from the multitude of diverse factors that the law in question must neglect. Thus each law inevitably has its errors, and these are just as necessary a part of its true significance as are those of its consequences that are correct [166].

It is important to repeat that for Bohm the errors referred to in the above quotation are not purely subjective phenomena; they possess an objective counterpart in the way in which the interplay between the elements of the relatively stable complexes as well as the qualities that have been left out delimits the validity of the laws describing the behaviour of the complexes. "It is clear from the above discussion" Bohm continues [166], "that scientific research does not, and cannot lead to a knowledge of nature that is completely free from error."

VIII

The application to *scientific method* is now quite straightforward. Nature is such that no law can ever be universally valid.

Hence, it is sound scientific method to restrict the laws we find to a certain domain [135]. It is unsound method to apply them outside this domain. And never should we be so bold as to proclaim a certain law as universally valid, i.e. as valid in all domains of experimentation, and under all possible conditions. On the other hand, if we are careful enough in our pronouncements about the applicability of a scientific theory, and if we always restrict it to its proper domain, we do not run the risk of being refuted by new discoveries. For "a new theory to which the discovery of . . . errors will eventually give rise, does not invalidate the old theories. Rather . . . it corrects the older theories in the domain in which they are inadequate and, in doing so, it helps to define the conditions under which they are valid" [31]. Only a philosophical idea, and not sound scientific method can lead to the attempt to apply a theory to every possible domain. Thus the assumption "that all the various levels, all qualitative changes, and all chance fluctuations will, eventually be reducible completely . . . to effects of some fixed . . . scheme of purely quantitative laws . . . is . . . essentially philosophical in character" [62]. More especially the assumption that Newton's laws are universally valid

> has implications not necessarily following from the science of mechanics itself, but rather from the *unlimited* extrapolation of this science. . . . Such an extrapolation is evidently . . . not founded . . . on what is known scientifically. Instead, it is in a large measure a consequence of a *philosophical* point of view . . . [37].

It is this methodological doctrine which I find highly questionable and which I shall attempt to criticise in the following last part of my review.

IX

First of all, how does Bohm justify his two basic cosmological principles, viz. the principles of the infinity of nature and the second principle that there exist complexes which are relatively stable over a certain period of time and which therefore allow for the description, in terms of finite sets of laws and concepts, of parts of nature? The principle of the infinity of nature he tries to justify partly by reference to experience which shows us a great variety of qualities; partly by reference to the history of science which shows that every set of laws has at some time been found to be valid in a restricted domain only; and partly by reference to the "basic spirit of scientific method itself, which requires that *every* feature be subjected to continuous probing and testing" [132]. The principle of the existence of complexes of relative independence and stability is again justified by reference to experience; but it is also justified by some kind of "transcendental" reasoning according to which in a world of a different structure the concept of a thing would not be applicable and science would be impossible [139 f.]. Now if we look at these arguments we find that they are all unsatisfactory. To start with, Bohm's methodological rules which have been stated above would forbid us to draw consequences from experience and to apply them universally. Yet this is just what is done in the first argument. The appeal to the history of science cannot be accepted either. For it could also have been used by the Aristotelians *against* the assumption that human knowledge gave at most an approximate account of what went on in nature. Thirdly the transcendental argument is not of the slightest use as long as we do not know whether our theories express knowledge or whether they are not only well fabricated dreams. But knowing this would presuppose knowledge of exactly those states of affairs whose existence is to be proved with the help of the argument. And finally the methodological argument is of no help either as it might well be the case that all the tests we carry out with respect to a certain theory lead to its corroboration and thereby to the corroboration of the idea that the world possesses a finite number of basic properties after all. We see, then, that Bohm's two basic principles are not supported by the arguments he uses in their favour. They are not even empirical, or scientific in Bohm's own sense [cf. 166] as he is not prepared to admit that they may be valid in a certain domain only and give way to some kind of mechanicism in all the remaining domains of experimentation. They represent an *absolute truth* which is not capable of improvement by taking into account errors [169 f.]. Yet they are cosmological principles, i.e. principles describing the basic structure of our world. This, then, is my first criticism: that there is not the slightest reason for not treating the most general cosmological principles, such as the principle of the infinity of nature on a par with less general laws. There is not the slightest reason for denying them the status of all the other laws, viz. their provisional character.

X

However it seems to me that this criticism does not yet go to the heart of the matter. For it leaves out one of the most important arguments that Bohm could adduce in favour of the absolute character of his two principles. I did not find the argument in the book, but I trust that it may be constructed along the following lines. Consider a law that is valid in a certain domain only. When this law is properly stated we shall soon discover its limitations. We are able to do so because there exists another domain which is not covered by the law, and whose presence is responsible for the errors it possesses. The conditioned validity of the law and its approximative character are thus wholly dependent upon the objective existence of such other domains. It would then seem to follow that for lack of domains outside the domain of its applicability a statement about "the infinite totality of matter in the process of becoming" [170] must be unconditionally and absolutely valid. It is this argument which will be the starting point of my second criticism.

It is assumed in this argument that the provisional and approximative character of a scientific law is *wholly* due to the objective limitations of the stability of the entities, or of the domain it describes. We must correct the law not because we had a wrong idea about the properties of the things described. We must correct it because these properties themselves are the relatively stable result of a very complicated interplay of an infinity of processes, and because they are therefore subject to slight changes and transformations. *But if we keep well within the domain of application of the law, then we cannot possibly be mistaken.*

This last principle has the following very interesting corollary: every description of nature that has ever been uttered is true within its domain, and conversely, it exhibits the existence of a domain to which it properly applies. There does not exist any description that is wholly mistaken and without a corresponding reality. Or, to express it differently—when describing our surroundings *we always speak the truth* (relative truth, that is), *and we are also always in contact with some part of reality.* Now this corollary has so little *prima facie* plausibility that I must defend it before trying to show its shortcomings. "Is it really the case," one may easily feel oneself inclined to object "that the savage who believes in, and claims to have observed, the actions of ghosts, tribal spirits, and the like is talking about entities which have some kind of existence in a restricted domain?" To this objection the retort may well be that a savage could not have described, or interpreted what he saw as indicating the existence of a ghost, if there had not been a justification for doing so. After all, he does not, *and cannot,* make arbitrary judgments in matters which may be of importance to his well being, and even to his life. Neither for him, nor for us would it be possible

> to choose the natural laws holding within a given degree of approximations, and in a particular set of conditions at will. . . . This does not mean that we cannot, in general, make our own choices as to what we will, or will not do. But unless these choices are guided by concepts that correctly reflect the necessary relationships that exist in nature, the consequences of our actions will not in general be what we choose, but rather something different [165].

In short, every theory of the universe, whether mythological or scientific in content, possesses some degree of truth, as the choice of a false theory would lead to undesirable consequences and would therefore be at once abandoned. *Nature itself forces man to speak the truth,* and it also forces him to speak in such a way that his theories have objective reference.

This, then, is the epistemology behind Bohm's belief that every theory, however absurd it may seem at first sight, has some kind of truth in it and correctly mirrors what exists in the universe: the ill success of a theory which is outright wrong and does not describe anything whatever is a corrective which after a very short time forces us to abandon it (if we were ever foolish enough to put it forth). Knowledge is a natural process which leads to a mirroring, in the head of man, of the properties of the universe. The mirror-image may be distorted at the edges. But first of all this distortion is due to a similar objective distortion of the processes in the world.

And secondly this distortion does not reach into the centre of the mirror which perfectly represents the situation at a certain level.

I do not believe that this account of our knowledge is a correct one. The simplest reason I can give for this contention of mine is that I believe man to be a little more whimsical and capricious than is assumed in the above picture of him. For in this picture it is assumed that *as a matter of fact* we recognise our mistakes, take them into account, and learn from them how to behave better. It is assumed that this process works like a well lubricated machine so that in the end whatever has been said contains some truth in it. (I suspect that a consistent elaboration of this epistemology will finally lead to the result that errors—subjective errors, that is—are never made: quite obviously Hegel's notorious "Alles Vernünftsgeist wirklich" is here lurking in the background.) But only a little knowledge of history will show that this assumption is factually false for at least two reasons. First, because there are enough examples of men, or of whole groups, who are not prepared to admit that they have been mistaken. And secondly because even death may not be a sufficient reason for changing ideas which have led to it. Quite on the contrary we often find, even in our own times, that ill success of an ill-conceived undertaking, and death resulting from it are both regarded as values and we also find the corresponding assumption that fate will sometimes deal roughly with its protégés. Furthermore, to turn to more theoretical considerations, is it not well known that refuting instances can with some ingenuity always be turned into confirming instances and that there exist elaborate theories which perform this transformation nearly automatically? Quite clearly such theories cannot be said to be in contact with reality and this in spite of their sophistication and in spite of the many fascinating statements they contain. From all this we have to conclude that *nature can never force us to admit that we have been mistaken.* Nor can it force us to recognise our mistakes. A mistake will be recognised as such only if first the conscious *decision* has been made not to make use of *ad hoc* hypotheses and to eliminate theories which do not allow of falsification. It is true that as a matter of historical fact this decision has been made by nearly all great scientists (although the present quantum theory seems to present an exception to this rule) . What is of importance here is that they never were, and never could be forced to proceed in that way, either by nature or by society.

XI

To sum up: at the back of Bohm's theory of knowledge there is the idea that facts and decisions both obey the same kind of laws, i.e. the laws of the material world in which we live. It is the idea that the development of moral codes, or of the laws which govern the non-moral behaviour of the members of a society, or that the development of knowledge is nothing but an aspect of the development of this material universe. This idea implies that neither the moral behaviour, not the social behaviour, nor even the status of our knowledge can be changed on the basis of an explicit decision. It is quite impossible to entertain a point of view which has no reference to any facts whatever. And it is equally impossible to introduce a new moral system unless it is somewhat related to situations already existent. This doctrine of *naturalism*[15] can be given various forms. It exists in a form which allows for the accommodation of the most revolutionary changes by simply asserting that these changes had already been prepared by the development either of the material universe or of society. In this form the doctrine is nothing but a verbal manoeuvre. Another form of the doctrine decrees that some existing pieces of knowledge, or of morals are unchangeable, because a change would amount to nothing less than a change of the unalterable course of events and of the laws which govern the universe. In this form the doctrine has very often been held by the defenders of the *status quo*. The simple logical point that decisions are never derivable from facts should show that in all its forms naturalism is based upon a logical fallacy. Now Bohm's own doctrine, although related to the doctrine of naturalism, is more detailed and less radical. He seems to admit that at times ideas may be invented which have very little to do with the facts. What he contends is, however, that these ideas will very soon be eliminated by a kind of natural selection which works either

---

[15] For an excellent discussion of this doctrine, its history, and its shortcomings see K. R. Popper, *The Open Society and Its Enemies* (Princeton, N.J.: 1954), Chap. V.

against those who hold them (they die), or against the ideas themselves (they are given up). That is, Bohm allows for deviations, but at the same time he assumes the existence of a corrective mechanism which quickly eliminates pipe-dreams and falsehoods. Now I want to show that although the doctrine in this form allows us to say that we sometimes speak the truth, it nevertheless does not give us any indication whatever as to which particular point of view expresses the truth. This we see when we ask the following important question: how long does it take this mechanism to eliminate a false hypothesis? Most certainly the length of time will depend upon the frequency with which the theory is tested, upon the decisiveness of the tests as well as upon the intention, on the side of the scientist, to take refutations seriously. Laziness and *ad hoc* manoeuvres may extend the periods of correction indefinitely. And the scientist, or whoever else is defending a certain point of view, need not perish in the course of events as he may well be careful enough to avoid tests which endanger his personal safety (there are numerous examples of this kind in the so-called "primitive" societies). Furthermore, who says that we shall at once stumble upon a refuting instance? But if this is so then Bohm's idea of the self-correcting character of knowledge does not help us at all to distinguish truth from falsehood. For all we know *all* our ideas may be quite thoroughly mistaken.

Now if this is the case, and if it is further admitted that we are able to discover our errors when trying to apply the ideas we possess (provided of course, we have first *decided* to give them a form in which they are testable, and we have also decided to take refutations seriously) then the only path open to us is that we must attempt relentlessly to falsify our theories. As we do not know which part of them is true, in what domain they are true, and whether they are true at all, we must attempt the falsification under all possible conditions. Testing them under all possible conditions means assuming *first* that they are *universally valid* and *then* trying to find out the limitations of this assumption. It is this fact that we never know to what extent our theories are correct which makes us first apply them universally. If we use a theory in this way we by no means assume, as Bohm seems to think (cf. his criticism of mechanicism, discussed above) that the theory *will be found to be correct* in all domains. The universal application of a theory means rather that *we are prepared to collect refuting instances from all domains.* The reason why I cannot accept Bohm's methodology of caution and why I prefer to it the methodology of falsification as it has been developed by Popper is therefore that the methodology of caution assumes the existence of things we know for certain, whereas I believe on the basis of the above consideration that this is much too optimistic a view of the status of our knowledge.

These, if I understand the book correctly, are the criticisms which I think must be made. But let me at once repeat that I do not therefore think the book to be of lesser value. Quite on the contrary, it is the repeated discussion and criticism of various points of view which leads to an advance of knowledge, and not the repetition of plain statements in which nobody can find any fault. To have in this way contributed to the theory of knowledge, and also to have shown the unity of (physical, philosophical etc.) knowledge is the great merit of the present book.

9

Classical and Non-Classical
Concepts in the Quantum Theory

by DAVID BOHM

EDITORIAL NOTE: *In reading this final essay, it is necessary to pay attention as much to the points of method and principle David Bohm raises as to the substantive suggestions he advances. In the very process of criticizing Heisenberg's position, he clarifies it strikingly, and his own proposed way ahead starts from a critical reappraisal of the presuppositions, brought to light in consequence. For instance, the emphasis placed on "observables" and on "relatively to the observer" in quantum mechanics has to be understood primarily as a reminder that the data of physics refer, not to isolated objects of study, but to complexes comprising both our ostensible objects of study and the apparatus within which they are being studied, and only secondarily as involving references to the "psychic states" of the scientific observer himself. In this respect, indeed, Bohm wishes to go even further than Heisenberg, who had still seen these "psychic states" as having a bearing on quantum physics, even if only a secondary one.*

More significantly, Bohm argues that the appeal to "complementarity" in the writings of Bohr and Heisenberg leaves the classical physics of Newton still enthroned in its Kantian sovereignty, at least over the world of everyday macroscopic experience, in a way for which he can find no warrant. (He even quotes Heisenberg—very surprisingly—as claiming that "the concepts of classical physics . . . are an essential part of the language . . . of all natural science.") As against Heisenberg's position, Bohm now wishes to advance to a new system of physical relationships that by-passes classical theory entirely. After all—as he argues, with some justice—the classical con-

cepts of which Heisenberg writes were already built around some very specific abstractions, for example, Cartesian co-ordinate geometry. If Saccheri's attempt to prove the unique validity of the Euclidean system had ended by refuting itself, what reason have we for thinking that Heisenberg's claim would not finally result in a similar reductio ad absurdum? *Instead, we should explore the possibility of relating our physical concepts directly back to the everyday experience of spatial characteristics, as ordered sets of topological relations.*

Whether the resulting concepts will bear fruit in physical theory at all quickly is still an open question today. All that matters here is Bohm's reminder that intellectual advance in physics can result just as well from better conceptual analysis as it can from more sophisticated mathematical inventiveness or more exact empirical observation. Einstein himself had inaugurated the theory of relativity by asking "What is there that we can mean *by the phrase '. . . at the same time as . . . ', when we are comparing events within different reference frames?" And this issue had been, essentially, an analytical rather than an observational or mathematical one. Once again, Bohm implies, we are as likely to see our way past the impasses of current quantum mechanics by better analysis as we are by devising better calculations or more ingenious experiments. If the position at which Bohm finally hints, with its references to the idea of "perspectives" and so on, raises echoes of Leibniz, this should be no particular surprise. For Leibniz, as well as being the inventor of the differential calculus in its modern form, was also the one great philosopher-mathematician in the age of Newton to challenge directly the intellectual authority of Descartes's geometrical foundation for mathematical physics and to offer instead an account of spatial characteristics built on the idea of "relations of co-existence," as seen from the viewpoint of a specific observer or "monad." To put the central point briefly, both classical and quantum physics had been alike committed to a Cartesian view of geometry; yet may we not be in a position now (Bohm asks) in which we should be exploring the possibilities opened up by the Leibnizian option?*

Physics and Philosophy[1] by W. Heisenberg makes a very useful contribution to the literature on the interpretation of the quantum

---

[1] W. Heisenberg, *Physics and Philosophy* (London 1959).

theory. It is of interest, first of all, because it can be regarded as an authoritative presentation of what has come to be known as the "Copenhagen" point of view (because of its assocation with Niels Bohr). Professor Heisenberg has played a leading role, both in the development of the quantum theory itself, and in the formulation of its interpretation according to the Copenhagen school. He is therefore eminently qualified to discuss this subject.

In view of the scarcity of clear expressions of the Copenhagen interpretation, this book is to be welcomed, particularly because in it many essential points which have hitherto been only implicit consequences of remarks in obscure articles are brought out openly and explicitly. By the same token, the author's efforts to relate his view to the natural science, the history of physics, and to philosophy in general, are illuminating, while his answers to criticisms of the Copenhagen interpretation will certainly be of interest to all those who are concerned with the subject, either from a scientific or a philosophical point of view.

Because this book presents the basic features of the Copenhagen interpretation in such a clear light, it constitutes a useful basis on which further criticisms of this intepretation can be developed. An article of this kind does not provide adequate space for an exhaustive analysis along these lines, but it may be of interest here to go into a few of the most important points involved.

First of all, with regard to the uncertainty principle, Heisenberg[2] brings out a point which has not been sufficiently emphasised elsewhere; namely, that the ambiguities which arise in the measurement process are only a special case of a universal ambiguity in the very mode of existence of everything. What is important here is not the impossibility of our obtaining perfectly precise knowledge about microsystems, which follows in a well-known way from the disturbance due to the quanta by which the apparatus must interact with the observed system. Rather, the essential point is, as Heisenberg states, that "a large part of the universe, including

NOTE: This article was originally planned as a review of *Physics and Philosophy* by Werner Heisenberg. But since Heisenberg and the author of this article actually have criticised each other before, and since this debate is partly continued by Heisenberg in *Physics and Philosophy*, it may be fairer to describe this article as an answer to Heisenberg rather than a review.

[2] *Op. cit.*, bottom of p. 52.

ourselves, does *not* belong to the object." (By "object," Heisenberg means here the particular object under investigation.)

It therefore appears to be recognised in this book that the underlying basis of the uncertainty principle is the real interconnection of everything in the universe, by means of quanta. Because these quanta are *indivisible,* they belong as much to one side of the connection as to the other. An essential aspect of what each thing *is* therefore lies in all other things, with which it is thus indivisibly related. From this, it follows that precisely definable modes of description of the detailed attributes of a thing (e.g. in terms of continuous mathematical variables) must be subject to a minimum degree of ambiguity, *this ambiguity being objective and universal, and not restricted just to the relationship between objects and observing apparatus.*

It follows from the above described point of view that the common notion of what is called an "object" must be changed in a fundamental way. For nothing (neither an electron nor an observing apparatus nor a man nor anything else) can correctly be regarded, even abstractly and conceptually, as having at each moment a complete and separate existence, the state of which is merely modified with the passage of time by its interaction with other things. Rather, as we have already indicated, there is an interpenetration in the very modes of existence of different things, such that only in the classical limit is the approximation of separately existing objects valid. This interpenetration can, in principle, include even a human being who observes the world and in the same act participates in it. It is with this possibility in mind that Heisenberg[3] calls attention to the need to give up the attitude which he calls "objectivisation," that is, the use of the concept of the separately existing object beyond its proper domain of validity. On the other hand, we are not thereby led to fall into the opposite error, termed by him "subjectivism," that is, the tendency to regard all our experience (e.g. measurements and observations) as referring only to our private knowledge and not to a real world of which we are a part. For in all cases of experimentation in physics (as well as in practical applications), the major source of interconnection with the observed system is by way of the apparatus, while the

[3] *Op. cit.,* p. 75.

human being has direct contact only with the latter, which being in the large-scale domain, is influenced in a negligible way by the contact. It follows then that in physics, the universe as a whole, *including the apparatus,* can for practical purposes be regarded as a separate object. However, no distinction between the object of investigation and the observing apparatus can be made at a quantum level of accuracy, nor can a perfectly sharp distinction be made between any two objects whatsoever in the universe, whether they are part of an experiment or not.

In the further development of his exposition of this notion, however, Heisenberg introduces ideas which do not seem to be entirely consistent with the above described point of view. Thus he states[4] that in the quantum theory the probability function (derived in the well-known way from the wave function) combines objective and subjective elements. It contains statements about possibilities or potentialities, which are "completely objective, not depending on any observer." However, he further asserts, the probability, "contains statements about our knowledge of the system, which are subjective insofar as they may be different for different observers." Moreover, he later goes on to say "the observation itself changes the probability function discontinuously; it selects of all possible events the actual one that has taken place." Therefore, he concludes, "the transition from the 'possible' to the 'actual' takes place during the act of observation." Thus Heisenberg seems to be saying here that whereas possibilities can exist outside the human mind, *actuality* can only be when someone perceives it.

In the next step, however, he recognises that this view is evidently not adequate, and in order to deal with this problem in another way, he introduces a distinction between the "psychic" and the "physical" act of observation.[5] He defines the physical act of observation as the process of interaction of the measuring apparatus with the observed system; and in this process, he further states:

> The transition from the "possible" to the "actual" takes place as soon as the interaction of the object with the measuring device, and thereby with the rest of the world, has come into play; it is not connected with the act of registration of the result by the mind of the observer. The dis-

4 *Op. cit.,* p. 53.
5 *Op. cit.,* p. 53.

continuous change in the probability function, however, takes place with the act of registration, because it is the discontinuous change of our knowledge in the instant of registration that has its image in the discontinuous change of probability function.

Heisenberg has thus brought into consideration two kinds of actualities,[6] namely, "the psychic" and the "physical." In order to bring out in more detail the kind of problem to which this leads, we shall consider specific examples of measurement of the position of an electron, with the aid of a set of Geiger counters arranged on a grid so as to cover the region of interest. Let us suppose then that the electron has already entered the system and triggered off one of the counters, but that no observer has yet looked to see *which* counter this is. Now, as Heisenberg indicated, at this stage one knows what are the objective physical *possibilities;* namely, that the counter in question must be one of those located where the amplitude of the electron wave function (and therefore the probability function) is appreciable. If, however, one tries to describe the fact that there is also what Heisenberg called "physical actuality" (viz. that among the above described possibilities, some counter has actually functioned), one discovers that there is no way in the theory to do so. For, as Heisenberg points out, the wave function, with its associated probabilities (which must, of course, contain all the information about the observed system that there can be) describes only "psychic" actualities. In other words, until an observer *actually perceives which counter has operated,* so that he can write a new wave function representing the actual state to which the previous possibilities have "collapsed" as a result of his perception, there is, as far as anything that can appear in the theory is concerned, no actuality at all, but only the above described set of possibilities.[7] The physical actualities introduced by Heisenberg

---

6 The word "actuality" refers, as its root implies, to some kind of *act*. In Heisenberg's discussion of the problem, this act is an observation.

7 This conclusion is not altered if we treat both the apparatus and the observed system quantum mechanically. For, in this case, there will be a wave function of the combined system, which after interaction is over, but before an observer has perceived the result, will still spread over the same range of possibilities as was obtained when we treated only the observed system quantum-mechanically. For a more detailed discussion, see, for example, D. Bohm, *Quantum Theory* (New York 1951), Chap. XXII.

therefore play no part whatsoever in the theory, since no predicted result would be changed in any way at all if the theory were developed without mentioning them. Nevertheless, Heisenberg evidently feels that it would not be permissible to leave them out of consideration altogether, for then we would be left only with "psychic" actualities, and therefore, with a subjectivist point of view, which he quite justifiably wishes to avoid. It would appear then that in order to keep away from subjectivism, he is ready to adopt the completely "metaphysical" assumption of physical actualities which play no part at all in the theory, but which are introduced only to avoid what he would otherwise regard as an untenable philosophical position.

If one wishes to deal with this problem in a more adequate way, it would seem almost inevitable that one will have somehow to introduce further physical conceptions and associated mathematical functions, which could represent the state of the "physical" actuality as existing outside the mind of the observer who perceives it. These new "actuality functions" would supplement the wave function, which latter would then constitute only one side of the theory. Naturally, the theory would have to be developed in such a way as to define the relationship between the actuality functions and the wave function, as well as to bring out the relationship of both to experiment. Of course, this could be done adequately only by in some way enriching, developing, and extending the laws of the quantum theory, so that the physical actualities would cease to be purely "metaphysical," and would instead play a real and essential role, both in the theory and in experiment.

It was on the basis of a consideration of the problem described above that the writer of this article was first led to criticise the Copenhagen interpretation. While trying to find a way to remedy the absence of "actuality functions" he developed a definite example of an alternative interpretation, which permitted the quantum theory to be extended so as to include them in a logically consistent way.[8] In this interpretation, it was proposed, in connection with an electron, for example, that in addition to the Schrö-

[8] D. Bohm, *Phys. Rev.,* 85 (1952), 166, 180. See also *Causality and Chance in Modern Physics* (London: Routledge, 1957).

dinger wave function, there was also a particle with a well-defined position and momentum, which interacted with the wave in a certain prescribed manner. The position of this particle plays the part here of an actuality function, in the sense that when the wave function spreads out over many possibilities, this particle determines which of these possibilities is actually present.

In his book, Heisenberg devotes considerable attention to the above criticism of the Copenhagen point of view as well as to many other criticisms that have been made by various authors. With regard to his discussion of the proposals described above (which alone will be considered here), Heisenberg's answer divides naturally into two parts.

In the first part,[9] he begins by objecting to various aspects of the model described above, stating that they are physically implausible and mathematically inelegant.[10] without, however, criticising either the logical consistency of the model, or its ability to account for all the phenomena that are treated in the Copenhagen interpretation. In doing this, he shows that he perhaps did not appreciate that the only purpose of this phase of the work was to show that an alternative to the Copenhagen interpretation is at least *logically possible*. If one such interpretation is possible, then it is very likely that others will be possible too. Therefore, it should be reasonable to go on, using the original model as a starting point, with the aim of developing a formulation that is more plausible physically and elegant mathematically. (Toward the end of this article, some results of the writer's further efforts in this direction will be indicated.)

At this point, however, Heisenberg raises another kind of objection, which leads him to question whether the above described programme is feasible at all. For, as he points out, the suggested new interpretation leads to precisely the same predictions for all experimental results as are given by the Copenhagen interpretation. Therefore, he argues that the introduction of the new particle variables, playing the role of actuality functions, is only a kind of

9 *Op. cit.*, p. 114.
10 In particular, he objects especially strongly to its failure to maintain certain kinds of symmetry in the formalism, such as that between position and momentum.

"ideological superstructure," which can never lead to anything physically new.

The possibility of such a criticism was, however, already taken into account by the writer of this review in the original articles referred to above (as well as in subsequent work on the subject). Indeed, with this problem in view, it was noted in these articles that the new interpretation constituted a broadening of the conceptual framework, permitting the introduction of a wide range of possible modifications, that could not even be expressed in the Copenhagen interpretation. Several illustrative examples of such modifications were actually outlined, but they were not described in detail, because the writer did not regard this particular model as a good basis for a definitive theory. Nevertheless, they were carried far enough to show that the suggested actuality functions (i.e. the particle variables) were capable of playing a part that could, in principle, lead to theoretical predictions that were quite different from those that are possible in the Copenhagen interpretation. It was also suggested that such differences would be important mainly in new domains not at present very well understood or investigated (e.g. that of short distances), while it was clear from the way the theory was formulated that the usual results could be obtained as a good approximation in the domain where the quantum theory has thus far been carefully studied.

It is in the second part of his discussion of this topic, however, that Heisenberg makes his main point with regard to the possibility of developing alternatives to the Copenhagen interpretation. For, as can be seen from his further comments[11] on the above described suggestions for modifying the quantum theory, he does not believe that this can be done in any way at all. He gives his reason in a quotation from Niels Bohr, saying that the expression of such an aim is similar to the sentence: "We may hope that it will later turn out that sometimes $2 + 2 = 5$." In other words, the proponents of the Copenhagen interpretation regard the development of any alternative to their point of view as logically impossible.

It must be emphasised, however, that the above contention is not proved, neither in Heisenberg's book nor elsewhere in the litera-

11 *Op. cit.*, pp. 117 and 118.

ture. Therefore, if we wish to criticise it, the best that we can do is first to explain it by reconstructing the probable lines along which such a proof might be attempted. In order to do this, we shall begin with the stress laid by Heisenberg[12] on the essential character for the Copenhagen interpretation of "the use of classical concepts in describing our experimental equipment and, more generally, in describing that part of the world which does not belong to the object." In the section following this quotation, it is made clear that by the term "classical concepts," one understands, firstly, space and time, and secondly, energy and momentum. In classical physics, the concepts of space and time refer to a kinematic description of the process of movement of matter; for example, the series of positions occupied by an object in a sequence of times. The momentum and energy concepts refer, however, to a description of the causal laws that hold in this movement; for example, Newton's laws, that the time rate of change of the momentum of a body is equal to the force applied to it (which leads in an isolated system to the conservation of momentum and energy). These laws are, of course, completely deterministic, in the sense that the initial positions and momenta of all the bodies of an isolated system completely determine the future behaviour of that system.

As is well known, in the quantum theory, the laws are not completely deterministic, but instead take the very different form of determining statistical relations. What is more important for our purpose here, however, is that the concepts (space, time, energy and momentum) in terms of which one expresses the experimental implications of quantum mechanical laws are nevertheless the same ones used in classical mechanics. In other words, as Bohr frequently emphasises,[13] the quantum theory introduces no new concepts into physics. What is new in this connection is, however, that *the old concepts, such as position and momentum, can be defined only within maximum limits of precision set by the uncertainty principle.* This ambiguity applies even to large-scale objects, but, of course, its consequences with respect to these are unimportant for practical purposes. Nevertheless, from the point of view of principle, the above described ambiguity plays a very significant part.

[12] *Op. cit.*, p. 82.
[13] Private communication.

For it means that from the experimental data entering into physics (and into any other science) one will be able to infer the properties of various parts of the universe to a maximum degree of precision which is exactly the same as that implied by the current quantum theory, when these properties are treated in the usual way in terms of wave functions, operators, etc. As a result there will be no room for the possibility of inferring anything of a different character (such as our proposed particle variables representing "actuality functions"), which would aim to add some new features to the description of the state of the system under observation, features that are not expressible in terms of the formalism of the quantum theory as it now stands. This would mean, however, that alternatives to the Copenhagen point of view could never have any additional experimental content, and so would be, as Heisenberg suggested, just "metaphysical" additions to the description, fulfilling no further function.

In view of the far reaching consequences of the conclusion described above, it is evidently important to ask what evidence there is in favour of its basic premise; namely, that the results of large scale experience must be expressed in classical concepts. In discussing this question, Heisenberg[14] states:

> The concepts of classical physics are just a refinement of the concepts of daily life and are an essential part of the language which forms the basis of *all natural science*.[15] Our actual situation is that we *do* use the classical concepts for the description of experiments. . . . There is no use discussing what could be done if we were other beings than we are.

It is clear from the above quotation that Heisenberg feels that classical concepts are inherent in all logical thinking about any subject whatsoever. Such a point of view implies that every understandable and describable aspect of experience could in principle be analysed by regarding the world as made up of various component parts, each having at any moment a definite position and a definite momentum. If we in practice do not do this in everyday life, but use other concepts instead, this means only that we are approximat-

14 *Op. cit.*, p. 55.
15 Italics added.

ing to the ideal of such a complete analysis (i.e. by "refining" these everyday concepts, we could come to nothing else but a suitable set of positions and momenta).

It must be admitted that ideas of the type described above are commonly held by physicists. It takes only a little reflection, however, to see that there are strong reasons suggesting that such ideas are false. To see why this is so, let us concentrate on an essential feature of the concepts of space and time as they are used in classical physics, namely, the description of the location of an object or an event in terms of a set of *continuous Cartesian co-ordinates*. Is it really true that we have no other way to think of space and time except in terms of such a concept? We may ask, for example, whether in everyday experience we would describe the location of a pencil by giving its precise latitude and longitude (which is what is implied by the above described "classical" concept of space). It is evident that we do not do this, but that instead, we describe the pencil as being on a certain desk, which is in a certain room, which is in a certain house, on a certain street, etc. In other words, we locate the pencil with the aid of a series of *topological relations,* in which one entity is *within* or *upon* another. The same is true of all laboratory experience. For in no experiment does one ever give an exact co-ordinate of anything (i.e. to an infinite number of decimals). Rather, in a typical measurement, one places a point *between* certain marks on a scale, thus once again locating it by means of a topological relationship. Indeed, in every experiment that can possibly be done, the notion of a precisely defined co-ordinate is seen to be just an abstraction, which is carried out when a topologically described experimental result is translated into the language of continuous co-ordinates.

It is clear then that behind the concept of space and time as described in terms of co-ordinates, there is a more fundamental topological concept, which lies at its basis, but which is usually just taken for granted without further discussion. For evidently, the idea of defining co-ordinates makes sense only if one presupposes that one knows what is meant by topological relations such as between, inside, outside, neighbourhood, etc. This is true not only with regard to the actual physical procedures by which measurements are carried out, but also with regard to the order of logical priority in the definition of the associated mathematical concepts. Thus, if the mathematical theory of space and time is to be developed in a natural way, it is well known that one must begin with topological relations, such as those described above,[16] and that only much later will one arrive at the concept of Cartesian co-ordinates (which is essentially a metrical notion).

We see then that Heisenberg's contention that classical concepts are the only possible refinements of everyday concepts must be false. For as shown above, one can at the very least obtain refinements leading to topological concepts, which are at once closer to everyday experience and more fundamental in a logical mathematical sense. (Of course, refinements of everyday concepts in still other directions should be possible too; but for physics, topology is particularly important, since it deals with the description of space and time, which play a central role in all physical theory.) We have therefore refuted the basic premise underlying the thesis of the inevitability of the Copenhagen interpretation, namely, that the only possible concepts are those of classical physics.

At this point, however, we are led naturally to go further, and to raise the question of just how topology can play an essential role in the quantum theory.[17] To do this, we shall give here a brief sketch of some of the lines along which the writer of this review has been developing a *topological formulation of the quantum theory*,[18] which constitutes a counter-example to the Copenhagen point of view. In this way, we shall be able to indicate how "non-classical" concepts can play a basic part in physical theory, making possible new kinds of experimental predictions which could not be considered within the framework of the Copenhagen interpretation, and which, according to Heisenberg's conclusions, should not be possible at all.

Our basic starting point in this formulation is that space and time are to be described by topological concepts (which are taken to be axiomatic) while concepts involving co-ordinates will play only a

---

[16] See, for example, A. Wallace, *Algebraic Topology* (London, 1957).

[17] The idea that there may be a fundamental relationship between quantum theory and topology was first suggested, to the author's knowledge, by L. L. Whyte. See, for example, his *Critique of Physics* (London, 1931).

[18] Some of the mathematical aspects of this formulation are still being developed, but it is expected that the work will be ready for publication in the near future.

secondary role. This means that we do not begin, as is done in some topological theories,[19] from continuous co-ordinates to which differential equations are assumed to apply "in the small" and then deduce topological relations "in the large." Rather, the fundamental equations with which we start must be expressed, from the outset, in terms of topological notions applying to *space and time* (such as before, after, between, inside, outside, overlap, boundary, path connectivity, etc.) .

The relation between continuous Cartesian co-ordinates and discrete topological concepts of the type described above can be brought out in more detail by means of the following highly simplified illustration. Consider an arbitrary point, P, on a string of unit length. We first fold the string in two. If P is on the right side of the fold, we assign it a "topological co-ordinate," C, $= 1$; if on the left, C, $= 0$. We continue to fold it some finite number, N, of times. In this way, we will obtain N topological co-ordinates for the point. These co-ordinates will give us a topological description of where the point is, which locates it as being within certain regions, which in turn are inside others, outside still others, etc. (Rather as with the case of the location of a pencil in common experience, as described previously.) In the limit as N approaches infinity, the set of the $c's$ can be used to define a continuous Cartesian co-ordinate, $x = \sum_{0}^{a} \frac{c_n}{2^n}$, (which expresses x as a binary decimal) . In the "classical"

point of view, we regard the limit of the above sum as the essential item of information, which must enter into the formulation of physical laws (e.g. in a differential equation) , while the process of summation of the infinite series is regarded as irrelevant for this purpose. On the other hand, in the topological point of view, we regard the coefficients of the series as containing the essential information which must enter into physical laws, while the sum of the series is considered to be only an abstraction (applicable in limiting cases when the number of elements is very large) .

It is clear then that the *laws* of physics will no longer be expressed as differential equations in a continuous set of Cartesian co-ordi-

---

[19] Such an approach to physics has recently been made by several authors; for example, J. A. Wheeler, *Phys. Rev.*, 97 (1955) , 511.

nates, but instead as topological relations in a discrete set of topological co-ordinates. Some clue as to the precise nature of these topological relations can be obtained from the existence of a remarkable analogy between the mathematics of topology and that of the modern quantum mechanical field theory (which is generally recognised to be the most definitive expression of the laws of the quantum theory available to date). Even with the simplified example of a topological co-ordinate given above, one can see the existence of some kind of analogy. For the fundamental field variables of the quantum theory contain "number of particle (Fermion) operators" associated with each point in space and time, which resemble our above described topological co-ordinates in having possible values that are either zero or unity. Thus, what is suggested is that perhaps the deeper meaning of these quantum mechanical operators is that they describe topological relations in space and time. This suggestion is in fact supported by a more detailed study (which we cannot enter into here), showing that certain groups which are basic in topology are also basic in the quantum mechanical field theory. From the group isomorphism, it is possible to show that our topological theory leads naturally, in the limit in which the approximation of continuous co-ordinates can be applied, to a Fermion field satisfying Dirac's equation (and of course, the Pauli exclusion principle).[20]

It appears then that the utilisation of the above described analogy can make possible the development of a topological formulation of the quantum theory, which while leading to the results of the usual quantum mechanics in suitable limiting cases, nevertheless possesses certain genuinely novel features, with regard both to its mathematical formulation and to its experimental predictions. In order to bring out in more detail what these novel features are, we first point out that in the topological formulation, a fundamental concept will be that of an *event*. In contradistinction to the "classical" axiom that fundamental events are to be described in the theory as mathematical points, we shall start with the axiom that all events (even those used in the expression of the basic laws of physics) are to be considered as constituting regions, having some

[20] Boson fields are also shown to have a certain topological significance, which we shall not, however, go into here.

spatial extension and temporal duration. ("Objects" will then consist of repetitive, persistent, and organised patterns of events.) A fundamental relationship into which such events can enter is that of *containment* of one event inside another. (For example, a flash of light can be in the space between a certain pair of marks on a ruler and occur while a given clock pointer is between a certain pair of marks on its dial.) This relationship replaces the classical one of coincidence, which evidently can be applied meaningfully only to point events. Of course, for the development of a physical theory it is not sufficient to specify the containment of one event in another. A whole system of containment relations is needed, which would in effect constitute an extension of the kind of topological co-ordinates that we have described above, so as to set up a fairly detailed topological description of what is commonly called the "space-time frame."

The next important concept is that of *elementary process.* An elementary process is a relationship between two different events, in which one becomes the other. Such an elementary process has by its very definition an aspect of *indivisibility.* For even though it is *potentially divisible,* if such a division were actually to be carried out, it would become a *different process.* (As for example, an egg can be divided by breaking it, but it thereby ceases to be an egg.) [21] In this way, we see that the basic quantum mechanical feature of the indivisibility of elementary processes fits naturally into topological concepts of space and time, whereas it does violence to the "classical" conceptions, which are inherently those of continuity.

From the elementary process, the next step is to consider the total cosmic process, in which all events that have been, are, and will be, are in principle taken into account, in their proper order (described topologically of course). Naturally, we cannot in practice specify all the details of this process; but as is done regularly in the science of cosmology, we can consider some model of the cosmos, which aims to treat only certain idealised and simplified systems of events, that are relevant in the discussion of some limited problem

---

[21] A similar result is obtained even in the Copenhagen interpretation. For example, by observing a quantum process, we can divide it as a result of the disturbance due to the measuring apparatus, but then it ceases to be the same process that was originally under discussion.

of interest (e.g. an experiment). In this connection, the observing apparatus, being a part of the cosmos that is evidently, in general, significant for the experiment, must also be described in the theory, at least in a suitably idealised and simplified way. (As, for example, Heisenberg did in his well known model of a highly idealised microscope with the aid of which he illustrated the uncertainty principle.) However, as we saw earlier, it is agreed, even by the proponents of the Copenhagen point of view, that at least in physics, the human observer can be left out of the description, since his act of perceiving the state of the large scale apparatus makes no significant change in the latter.

The system of events described above is then the "physical actuality" that, we saw previously, Heisenberg felt to be necessary, even though in the Copenhagen point of view, it plays no physical role. In the topological formulation, however, the situation is different. For here one *begins* with the actual process with all its events in their proper order. To each event in the process, one then associates a particular wave function, characteristic of that event. In effect, every such event is regarded as furnishing a unique and individual perspective on the cosmic process (in the sense that in a certain way it "perceives" its past, in the form of a trace or a set of marks left by this past in this particular event). As a detailed development of the theory shows, the perspective of a given event is represented mathematically by the wave function associated with that event. This wave function then determines potentialities for the development of the cosmos subsequent to the event in question.

It is clear from the above discussion that in our formulation of the quantum theory, there is an inexhaustible set of wave functions (one for each event), whereas in the usual formulation, there is, as is well known, only one wave function (or at most, one for each observer). To relate the way the wave function appears in both points of view, we note that in our theory, the (large scale) events which are the results of the functioning of a particular piece of apparatus furnish their own special perspective on the cosmic process. When an observer looks at the apparatus (of course, without changing it significantly) and perceives these events, he can, if he wishes, adopt as his own the perspective on the cosmic process that is implied by the events in question, and with it the corresponding special associated wave function. This wave function implies potentialities for the future development of the system under discussion, in the same way as happens in the usual formulation of the theory, and therefore plays a role analogous to that of the wave function as it appears in the Copenhagen interpretation. It is clear, however, that our point of view differs from that of the Copenhagen interpretation in the essential respect that in it, the wave function does not primarily represent "psychic" actuality (i.e. the perception of the event by an observer), but rather, "physical" actuality (i.e. the perspective of the associated event on the cosmic process).

The introduction of one wave function for each event must lead, of course, to new features, both in the mathematical formulation of the theory, and in the mode of relating it to experiment. Thus, with regard to the formulation, it is evidently necessary to ensure that the potentialities implied by the wave function of any one event are compatible with those implied by the wave functions of all the other events, so that they will fit together to make a coherent whole. The steps needed to satisfy this requirement lead in fact to a further mathematical development, into the details of which we shall not enter here. In essence, however, what is done is to determine the future of a given set of events as the logical intersection of all the potentialities implied by this set of events (i.e. what is common to all these potentialities). A little reflection will show that this idea is quite natural, being only a refinement of what is done in "common sense" with regard to similar problems. For we are merely requiring that actuality be that which is possible, according to every valid perspective. The determination (or limitation of range of possibilities) brought about in this way need not be complete, but as more perspectives are taken into account, it can in general go beyond the limits set by the uncertainty principle, which latter follow when we suppose that only a single perspective is available.

The type of determination described above is quite different from that appearing either in classical theory or in quantum theory. For in the latter two theories, the basic procedure is to start with some initial conditions (e.g. precise positions and momenta in classical theory, or a definite "quantum state" in quantum mechanics), and then to predict the corresponding entities to be found in a future experiment. As a result, one simply discards a great deal of information contained in the *observable sequence of events* leading up to the initial conditions; for it is effectively assumed that nothing matters except the initial conditions themselves, independently of the process in which they came to be what they are. On the other hand, there is no logical justification for discarding the additional information which is in the order of this sequence (beyond of course, the practical one that in a certain limited range of phenomena in which current theories are satisfactory, this order is found not to be relevant). And indeed, in the topological formulation of the quantum theory, the additional information described above is taken into account. For in this formulation, the sequence of actual events not only appears directly in the fundamental mathematical laws (which are expressed in terms of the wave functions associated with each event in the sequence), but it also appears as part of the basic empirical data of any problem (because the observed sequence helps to determine, or at least to limit, the wave functions described above).

We conclude then that, contrary to what is maintained in the Copenhagen interpretation, the quantum theory can be developed further to introduce the notion of a "physical actuality," with a new experimental and mathematical content not expressible in the usual formulation, and nevertheless approaching the current theory in those domains in which the latter has really been well confirmed. In order to achieve this result, however, we have been led to introduce topological concepts that are quite different from those appearing in classical physics and in the Copenhagen interpretation of the quantum theory. The applicability of such topological concepts is not restricted to the micro-domain, but rather, extends through every level, including the large scale level of common experience. For example, the movement of a particle is no longer to be described in terms of the classical concepts of position and momentum, but rather in terms of a series of discrete events.[22] The events are so close together in space and time, however, that for a certain limited range of practical purposes, they may be treated on the large scale level as forming a continuous orbit. (As the pressure

[22] The change between one event and its successor takes the place of the concept of momentum.

216   DAVID BOHM

on a macroscopic object, due to a rain of molecules on its surface,
can similarly be treated as continuous for some purposes, even
though we must keep the actual atomic constitution of matter in
mind when we are trying to understand pressure in a fundamental
way.)

It follows then that the use of topological concepts implies the
need for a re-evaluation of the significance of *every aspect of physics*
including not only the current quantum theory but also classical
mechanics. When this re-evaluation is accomplished, however, it is
discovered that we are simply giving up the excessively abstract
classical notion of Cartesian co-ordinates, and returning to a topological notion of space and time that is very close to one that we
have always been using in common experience.

Contributors and Sources

MAX PLANCK, "The Unity of the Physical World-Picture," originally delivered as a lecture to students in the science faculty at the University of Leiden (Holland) on December 9, 1908, and published as "Die Einheit des physikalischen Weltbildes," *Physikalische Zeitschrift,* 10 (1909), 62–75; and "On Mach's Theory of Physical Knowledge," originally published as "Zur Machschen Theorie der Physikalischen Erkenntnis," *Physikalische Zeitschrift,* 11 (1910), 1186–1190. Used here by permission of the estate of Max Planck and Methuen & Co. Ltd. Newly translated by Ann Toulmin. The late Professor Planck (1858–1947) is best known as the man who solved the outstanding difficulties in the Maxwellian theory of "black-body" radiation, by suggesting that radiant energy of any particular frequency f, is emitted from material bodies only in "quanta" of energy, $E,$ of a size directly proportional to f—the constant of proportionality being denoted as h and referred to as "Planck's constant." But he made several other distinguished contributions to theoretical physics, and his essay *A Scientific Autobiography* is one of the best examples of its kind. Professor Planck was awarded the Nobel Prize for Physics for 1918.

ERNST MACH, "The Guiding Principles of My Scientific Theory of Knowledge and Its Reception by My Contemporaries," originally published as "Die Leitgedanken meiner naturwissenschaftlichen Erkenntnislehre und ihre Aufnahme durch die Zeitgenossen," *Scientia,* 7 (1910), no. 14, 2 ff, and *Physikalische Zeitschrift,* 11 (1910), 599–606. Newly translated by Ann Toulmin. The late Professor Mach (1838–1916) was a scientist and philosopher of great versatility. Much of his early research was concerned with the empirical study of perception, but he made a name subsequently both as an empiricist philosopher of science (in which capacity he was a dominant influence on twentieth-century logical empiricism in Vienna, and later in the U.S.A.), and for his research on the propagation of the shock waves from explosions. The latter became an integral part of the theory of supersonic flight, in which the standard measure of supersonic speed (velocity of aircraft, divided by the velocity of sound) is still referred to as the "Mach number." Professor Mach's chief publications are listed in the essay reprinted here.

T. PERCY NUNN, "Anthropomorphism and Physics," *Proceedings of the British Academy,* 14 (1927), 13–45. Originally delivered as the Henriette Hertz annual philosophical lecture before the British Academy on December 15, 1926. Copyrighted by Oxford University Press; reprinted by permission. T. Percy Nunn (Sir Percy Nunn, 1870–1944) was Professor of Education at the University of London from 1913 to 1936. He specialized in the teaching of mathematics and physical science, and wrote extensively both on educational topics and on popular science and philosophy of science. His books included *The Aims of Scientific Method* (1907) and *Relativity and Gravitation* (1923).

MORITZ SCHLICK, "Causality in Contemporary Physics," *British Journal for the Philosophy of Science,* 12 (1961–2), 177–193 and 281–298. Translated by David Rynin from the original essay published in *Die Naturwissenschaften,* 19 (1931), 145 ff. Copyrighted by Cambridge University Press; reprinted by permission of the Press and the translator. Moritz Schlick (1882–1936) was originally educated as a physicist, but his chief work was as a philosopher of science. Having succeeded in 1922 to the professorship at Vienna earlier held by Mach, he was for more than a decade the man around whom the activities of the Vienna Circle turned. He wrote a number of significant books, on relativity, epistemology and ethics, but his chief influence was through his personal character and teachings. His assassination by an insane student, while he was still in mid-career, precipitated the break-up of the Vienna Circle group which was completed by Hitler.

A. EINSTEIN, B. PODOLSKY and N. ROSEN, "Can Quantum-Mechanical Description of Physical Reality Be Considered Complete?", *Physical Review,* 47 (1935), 777–780. Reprinted by permission of the Estate of Albert Einstein, the authors and publishers. Albert Einstein (1879–1955) is known most widely for his two theories of relativity, published in 1905 and 1916 respectively. But he made major contributions to several branches of physics, and his explanation of the photo-electric effect as evidence for particles of electromagnetic radiation ("photons") transformed Planck's idea of "quanta" from a minor amendment to Maxwell's theory of electromagnetism into the foundation of twentieth-century quantum theory. His criticisms of the foundations of later quantum mechanics, as summarized here, were therefore the views of a man who had been a major contributor to the very developments he was discussing; and the dispute was carried on later, at much greater length, in the volume *Albert Einstein, Philosopher-Scientist* (ed. P. A. Schlipp). The present paper was written at the Princeton Institute for Advanced Study in collaboration with two of his students: the late Professor B. Podolsky, who subsequently taught at Cincinnati, and Professor Rosen, who now teaches at Haifa (Israel).

N. BOHR, "Can Quantum-Mechanical Description of Physical Reality Be Considered Complete?", *Physical Review*, 48 (1935), 696–702. Reprinted by permission of the Estate of Niels Bohr, the author and publishers. Niels Bohr (1885–1965) was one of the dominant figures in atomic physics from early in the century until well after World War II. He did his first important work under Ernest Rutherford, with whom he is linked as coauthor of the first quantum theory of sub-atomic structure—the so-called Rutherford-Bohr planetary model of the atom. But unlike Einstein and Rutherford, Bohr continued to play a large part in the development of quantum theory after the introduction of Werner Heisenberg's and P. A. M. Dirac's new system of quantum mechanics in the years 1925 to 1927. Indeed, the chief school of orthodox quantum mechanics from the 1930's on (leaving aside the war years, when Bohr escaped from Denmark to Britain and the U.S.A.) was that which centered on Bohr's Institute for Theoretical Physics in Copenhagen. Niels Bohr wrote extensively about physics, and also tried—less satisfactorily—to extend his "principle of complementarity" to broader philosophical problems.

N. R. HANSON, "The Copenhagen Interpretation of Quantum Theory," *American Journal of Physics,* 27 (1959), 1–15. Copyrighted by the American Association of Physics Teachers; reprinted by permission. The late Professor Hanson (1924–1967) studied at the University of Chicago, Columbia University and the University of Oxford. He taught philosophy and history of science at Cambridge University and Indiana University, and was Professor of Philosophy at Yale University at the time of his tragic death, in a crash of his private airplane, in April, 1957. Norwood Russell Hanson wrote two striking books, *Patterns of Discovery* (1958) and *The Concept of the Positron* (1962), as well as many papers in philosophical and scientific journals. He was beginning to do some novel work on the history of aerodynamics when this was cut short by his death.

P. K. FEYERABEND, "Professor Bohm's Philosophy of Nature," *British Journal for Philosophy of Science,* 10 (1959–60) , 321–338. Copyrighted by the Cambridge University Press and the author; reprinted by permission. Paul Feyerabend is currently Professor of the History and Philosophy of Science at University College, London. He obtained his doctorate in Vienna, and has taught philosophy in Britain, Germany and the United States, where he was for several years at the University of California, Berkeley. He has published numerous influential papers and essays on topics in philosophy of science and epistemology, many of them extending a line of attack analogous to that of Karl Popper into the general theory of knowledge. He has played a leading part in the philosophical discussion about quantum mechanics.

DAVID BOHM, "Classical and Non-Clasical Concepts in the Quantum Theory," *British Journal for Philosophy of Science,* 12 (1961–2) , 265–280. Copyrighted by the Cambridge University Press and the author; reprinted by permission. David Bohm is currently Professor of Theoretical Physics at Birkbeck College, London. He obtained his doctorate at the University of California, Berkeley, and has taught physics at Princeton University, at São Paulo (Brazil) and Haifa (Israel) , as well as in Britain. David Bohm's book on *Quantum Theory* (1951) is among the best and most authoritative expositions of the subject. This makes his subsequent attempts to work beyond orthodox quantum mechanics to a deeper level—exemplified in his *Causality and Chance in Modern Physics* (1957) and many recent papers—that much more interesting.

STEPHEN TOULMIN is Professor of Philosophy at Michigan State University. His numerous books on philosophy and the history of science include *The Philosophy of Science, Foresight and Understanding* and *The Architecture of Matter* (with June Goodfield) . He is also editor of the symposium, *Quanta and Reality.*

70 71 72 73   12 11 10 9 8 7 6 5 4 3 2 1